# of The Cid

Robert C. Goldston

Illustrated by Stephane

THE **BOBBS-MERRILL** COMPANY, INC.
A SUBSIDIARY OF HOWARD W. SAMS & CO., INC.
Publishers • INDIANAPOLIS • NEW YORK

Library of Congress Catalog Card Number: 63-19010
Copyright © 1963 by Robert Goldston
Printed in the United States of America
First Edition

The Legend of The Cid

The Legend

¡Para Maximiliano, que sea Caballero!

CONTENTS

The Legend of The Cid

How The Cid
Won His Knighthood

Pues, señor, very many years ago—almost one thousand, in fact—Spain was a land of constant wars. The best part of the country: the rich green *huertas* of Andalucia, the fine fishing coast of the Levante, the valleys that lie like jewels at the feet of the snow-capped *Sierra Nevada*; all these were in the hands of the Moors. These Moors were a fierce and warlike tribe of Moslems who had crossed the Straits of Gibraltar from Africa many years before. On their swift Arabian horses, armed with lances and curving scimitars, they shouted as they rode into battle, "Allah is God and Mohammed is His only Prophet!" They had crushed the Christian Gothic Kingdoms of Spain and seized most of the country. Then they settled down to enjoy their conquests. They built many fine palaces and cities, and with their science of irrigation they converted many deserts into rich farmlands. But like conquerors before and since, they were softened by their victories. They set up small, independent kingdoms and fell to quarreling amongst themselves.

The Spaniards had been forced back into the bleak mountains
of Galicia and Asturias far to the north. Their lands were the
desert plains of Castille and Navarre, the rocky soil of Leon and
Aragon, and their cities were grim fortresses. As victory had
softened the Moors, so defeat had made the Spaniards into a
race of hardy warriors. Their great ambition was to reconquer
their land and drive the hated Moors back into Africa. The
task was long and cruel; many thought it would be impossible.
But the greatest enemy that the Spaniards had to face was their
own jealousy and disunity.

For in that time Christian Spain was divided into many
small and independent kingdoms. There was a Kingdom of
Castille, a Kingdom of Leon, a Kingdom of Navarre, a Kingdom
of Aragon—in fact, there were as many kingdoms in Spain as
there were provinces, and they spent as much time fighting
each other as they did making war on the Moors.

The most powerful of all the Christian kings of Spain in those
days was Fernando I, King of Castille and of Leon. He received
tribute from the kings of Aragon and Navarre, and even from
the Moorish Emirates of Toledo and Zaragoza. In his youth he
had been a mighty warrior and in his old age he was a just
and benevolent monarch, loved by his people and respected by
his enemies. It was his dream to see Spain united, but as the
years passed he realized that this would not happen during
his lifetime. So he took thought to the education of his sons.
Perhaps they would be wise and strong enough to finish the
task he had begun.

One day in mid-winter, King Fernando was seated in private
council with several of his advisors. The old king wore a heavy
coat of ermine, and a bearskin rug covered his knees, for although the small council room was hung with tapestries, yet the
icy winds blew through its portals. The king's great jeweled
sword of state rested against the arm of his chair and he stroked

his long white beard thoughtfully as he discussed affairs of state. Suddenly a commotion broke out in the corridor outside the council chamber.

The king's brows gathered in anger. "Who dares to disturb a council meeting?" he roared. "Guards! Bring the culprit before me!"

Two soldiers, who always stood behind the king's chair, hastened to obey. Soon they returned with three young nobles. King Fernando's face reddened with embarrassment when he saw that they were his own sons, the Princes Sancho, Alfonso and Garcia. Their clothes were torn and their faces bloody.

"What does this mean?" cried the king. "Am I to be insulted by my own sons? Are there royal princes in Castille who know no better than to disturb a council meeting? Explain yourselves!"

The three lads bowed their heads and looked reproachfully at one another. Finally Alfonso, who was the eldest, spoke out. "Sire, Sancho has said that upon your death he will inherit the Kingdom of Castille and I will inherit the Kingdom of Leon. But as the first born I am entitled to inherit all your lands!"

"You won't know how to defend them!" Sancho broke in angrily. He wiped a bit of blood from his face and glared at his brother.

"And you, Garcia?" the king demanded. "Have you also been dividing up my kingdom before I die?"

Garcia, who was the youngest of Fernando's sons, shook his head sadly. "No, Sire. I only tried to make peace between my brothers. But I could not. Besides, they said they would divide my inheritance between them after you died!"

King Fernando stroked his beard and stared at his sword of state. When at last he spoke, his face was hard as stone. "We see now that the royal princes have been suffering from idleness," he said gravely. "We shall remedy that situation. Since they also seem to have forgotten their manners, we shall send them to a fitting school for instruction. It is our command that the royal princes report at once to our stables and there work as grooms until the feast of Saint John. Perhaps they will learn better manners from our noble Castillian horses. Begone!"

The three lads bowed politely and left the room, glancing neither to the one side nor the other, so great was their shame.

When they had gone, King Fernando picked up his sword of state and rested it across his knees. He stared at it sadly and thoughtfully. The silence among his advisors was complete. Finally he raised his head and said, "This may be in great part our own fault. The question of the inheritance ought to be settled at once. Our days are drawing to an end and we would not leave our kingdom a prey to civil wars."

The king rose to his feet. "We hereby command that heralds be sent to every part of our kingdom and every place therein. They shall command all of our subject nobles and faithful vassals to attend a great Council of State which will be held before us on the feast day of the Holy Saint John, the Blessed Baptist. At this council we shall decide the future of our kingdom."

Now the king's advisors broke their silence. Some begged him to reconsider such a hasty decision. Others maintained that he had yet many years before he need think of inheritances.

But King Fernando simply shook his head. "We are accustomed to speaking only once," he declared, and so ended the matter.

Far and wide the king's heralds sped with the tidings. To the sound of trumpets, the royal command was made known throughout his kingdom. All the king's subject nobles made preparations to present themselves at the royal court on the day of Saint John.

One of the lesser of these nobles was don Diego de Vivar. He was a very learned and wise man, full of years, who lived in seclusion with his family near the city of Vivar. On more than one occasion he had been called to advise the king about affairs of state. Yet his greatest pleasure was in teaching his wisdom to his sons and watching them grow into stalwart manhood.

The royal herald found don Diego seated in his library surrounded by books and maps and manuscripts. The old scholar listened courteously to the herald's announcement, glanced wistfully at his manuscripts, and then sighed. "You may tell His Majesty that I have heard and will obey his command," he said. But when the herald had left, don Diego muttered to himself, "And yet I prefer the company of these manuscripts to the company of kings." It was just at that moment that Rodrigo, don Diego's eldest son, burst into the room. His eyes sparkled and his breath was quick. He had been practicing swordplay and his tanned skin was beaded with sweat. "Pardon me, Father, I saw the king's herald ride by."

Don Diego looked up. Rodrigo was his favorite son and yet he was as different from his father as red wine is from white. His whole interest was in fighting. Archery, swordplay, lancing, riding—these were Rodrigo's favorite studies. And although the lad was only seventeen, yet his body was muscled and tall as a man's. "Indeed?" don Diego demanded severely. "And so you immediately left your practice to interrupt my studies?"

"Is there to be war, Father?" Rodrigo asked.

"Thanks be to God, no, there is not to be war, although I know you would like nothing better. Instead, there is to be a great Council of State. I must present myself before the king on the feast day of Saint John."

"Father, may I come?"

"No! Absolutely not. You have not been invited. You are not a noble, and I do not imagine that His Majesty requires the advice of a seventeen-year-old boy!"

15

Rodrigo blushed. "But the journey to the royal court is a long one, Father. You might meet bandits or Moors on the way. I could protect you."

Don Diego laughed. "It is true that I am an old man, but I am too poor to be molested by bandits, and there are no Moors between here and the royal court."

"But you might run into a raiding party, and besides—well, Father, if I do not ever meet the king, he will not know I exist, and I'll never be knighted!"

Don Diego shook his head patiently. "You are still too young to be knighted. As far as raiding parties are concerned, may I remind you that you have only your wooden practice sword, and we have only one horse? Perhaps you think I ought to walk while you ride *Pitiuso* to protect me from imaginary Moors with your wooden sword?"

"No, Father. I could ride behind you on *Pitiuso* and if we were attacked I would use your sword, *Tizone.*"

"Enough!" Don Diego raised his hand. "While you have been babbling I have been thinking. I will indeed take you to the great Council."

"Thank you, Father."

"Silence! I will take you not for protection against ferocious Moors or to have you make a fool of yourself by asking the king to knight you. You shall accompany me to the royal court so that you may see for yourself what a tiresome thing it is. It will be an education for you. And may I remind you ——"

Don Diego started to lecture Rodrigo in the principles of courtesy practiced at the court of Fernando I, but Rodrigo scarcely listened. In his excited imagination he had already saved his father from bandits and was about to lead the king's entire army in a great charge against the legions of the Moors.

Preparations were made. Rodrigo's mother made him a new cloak of crimson. Rodrigo himself polished *Pitiuso's* high-backed

saddle and reins until they gleamed like ebony. He was so impatient for the journey to begin that he could not sleep at night, but would practice thrust and counterthrust with his wooden sword until sunrise. Don Diego, meanwhile, busied himself in preparing a detailed history of Castille which he intended to present as a gift to King Fernando.

On the day of their departure, Rodrigo's mother, his younger brothers, Hernan and Bermudo, and the three old servants who had been with the family for many years came out to see them off. *Pitiuso,* although an old horse, held his head proudly and pawed impatiently at the ground. Rodrigo, his new cape clasped over his shoulders, kissed his mother farewell. Don Diego mounted *Pitiuso,* bade his wife good-by, cleared his throat and then made a lengthy speech during which he recounted most of the history of Spain and ended by commending his family to the care of God. Then he motioned Rodrigo to mount behind him on *Pitiuso* and at long last they departed.

The journey from Vivar to the royal capital at Burgos was not a long one, but the lands they had to cross were rocky and barren and the roads were few and badly maintained. Because *Pitiuso* carried a double load, they could proceed no faster than the horse could walk. Don Diego passed the time instructing Rodrigo on the customs of the places they passed through. Rodrigo listened courteously, but his eyes were always roving to the distant mountains as if he expected a band of Moors to ride forth at any moment.

When evening came they stopped at a small inn by the side of the road near the city of Valladolid. While don Diego made arrangements for a room, Rodrigo took *Pitiuso* to a nearby well to water him. He found several soldiers with horses waiting at the well and they talked of various matters but especially of the endless wars against the Moors. Rodrigo listened and wished in his heart that he too were a veteran to speak of battles and sieges. While the soldiers were talking there suddenly came a cry from nearby, "Is there no Christian who will help me?"

Rodrigo and several of the soldiers rushed to find the voice. Soon they came upon a leper who had sunk into a patch of quicksand. The leper was badly hurt and had already sunk in up to his waist.

"For the love of God," he cried piteously, "give me a hand to free me from this pit!"

But when the soldiers saw the terrible ravages of leprosy on the man's face and arms they recoiled in horror.

But Rodrigo's heart was touched. Leaning over the quicksand he stretched out his arms, gripped the leper's hands and with a mighty pull drew him forth. It was then he saw that the man was almost naked and shivered desperately in the cold. Taking

off his new cloak, he wrapped it around the leper's shoulders and said, "They will not allow you to stay at the inn, but if you wish you can sleep in the stables next to my horse *Pitiuso*. The straw is warm and I will bring you food."

"Thank you, my son," the leper answered. "It is not only by fighting that one gains heaven."

After seeing the leper safely to the stable, Rodrigo returned to the well to find *Pitiuso*. The soldiers drew away from him when he approached. "You may already be infected!" they cried. "You must be seeking death to touch a leper!"

Rodrigo shrugged. "Only what God wills may come to pass," he answered.

Then he gave water to *Pitiuso* and returned to the stable. He saw the leper sleeping on his cape, huddled in the straw. As he combed and groomed *Pitiuso* he decided that he would have to bring food secretly to the poor man for he feared that his father would react as the soldiers had.

A few hours later, after they had eaten, and while his father snored loudly on the bed next to him, Rodrigo arose, gathered together the bread and meat he had saved from his own meal and made his way to the stable. It was now past midnight. But when he arrived he found that the leper had disappeared. There was his cape, folded neatly beside *Pitiuso*, and there was the depression in the straw where the man had slept. But the leper himself had disappeared. Rodrigo was just about to return to the inn when he heard a voice behind him.

"Were you seeking me, Rodrigo?"

Rodrigo whirled and saw, standing at the stable entrance, a man dressed in an immaculate white tunic. A soft glow of light bathed the man's body although there was no moon that night. "Who are you?" Rodrigo asked in a trembling voice.

"Do not be afraid, Rodrigo. I am Saint Lazarus," the apparition said. "It was I whom, for the love of God, you saved this day.

In reward for your faith I am permitted to tell you that from this time forth you shall be invincible. Your fame will increase from day to day, and when you die it shall be with honor. As our Lord rescued me from the tomb, so has it been given to you to win a great victory even after you die." The apparition smiled, raised its hand in benediction and then vanished.

Rodrigo returned to the inn, but he slept not at all that night. As he thought of this strange happening he was certain of only one thing; he would never tell any living man of what had come to pass.

The next day passed in hot and dusty journeying. Don Diego never ceased lecturing and Rodrigo's eyes were forever sharp for the distant cloud of dust that might announce bandits or Moors. Another night at another inn and still another day came and went while they made their way slowly beside the green banks of the *Rio Pisuerga*. It was late in the afternoon of the third day, when the sun glinted red on the distant peaks of the *Sierra Cantabria*, that *Pitiuso* suddenly reared and stopped short.

Within a minute Rodrigo had jumped down and was running toward a nearby outcropping of rock. There, behind the escarpment, a nest of bandits might be waiting to fall upon them. Don Diego called after his son, but Rodrigo paid no heed. He climbed cautiously up the side of the escarpment and peered down. Then he stood up and laughed. His band of robbers was nothing more than a wild and starving horse, munching peacefully on the sparse grass in the shade of the rocks. He was a stallion, thin and uncombed, without a saddle. When Rodrigo approached, the horse allowed him to pat its neck. It was obviously not a wild horse, but one that had been abandoned or whose owner had met with misadventure.

By this time don Diego had ridden up on *Pitiuso*. "What a sorry-looking beast!" he exclaimed. "It has been alone for a long time."

"In that case it may as well be mine!" Rodrigo cried.

Don Diego laughed. "You would have to be a *babieca* indeed to want so forlorn a horse!" he said. By *babieca* he meant fool.

"So be it. I will have this horse and I shall call him *Babieca* and one day all the world will know of him!" Rodrigo ran his hands through the horse's tangled white mane.

"Well, it will be a rest for *Pitiuso*," don Diego admitted. "Take the horse if you will, but I fear that all the world will come to know of him as a joke."

Rodrigo spoke softly to the stallion and then quickly mounted. "You see, Father, he permits me to mount!"

"He simply hasn't the strength to run away. You will make a fine sight riding into the royal court on a horse like that!"

"By the time we arrive in Burgos, *Babieca* will look as well as *Pitiuso*."

And Rodrigo kept his word. That night he spent hours combing and grooming *Babieca* and each day and night for the rest of the journey he fed him prodigiously. He even managed to buy an old cavalry saddle from a soldier at one of the inns and he polished it until it sparkled. By the time they arrived before the walls of Burgos, *Babieca* was a proud and well-groomed horse.

On the feast day of Saint John, Rodrigo accompanied his father to the great Hall of Justice in the royal palace. It seemed to him as they entered that he had plunged into a sea of color. The high stone walls of the hall were hung with brilliant tapestries. The fiery banners and pennants of Castille and Leon hung overhead from golden staffs. Ranks of soldiers in sparkling armor lined the hall with their lances raised, looking like a silver-tipped forest. So crowded was the hall with knights, counts, dukes and peers, all wearing brilliantly colored capes and plumed helmets, that it seemed as if all the nobility of the kingdom were present. And that was very nearly true. Here were the tributary kings of Navarre and Aragon, the Royal Princes

Sancho, Alfonso and Garcia; there were the famous knights
Arias Gonzalo, Peransules and Diego Lainez. And at the end of
the hall Rodrigo could see King Fernando himself, seated upon
a golden throne, the great jeweled sword of state resting across
his knees while his bearded head inclined patiently to the long
line of nobles who pressed forward to do him honor.

Rodrigo's eyes, sweeping this glittering pageant, suddenly
came to rest on a nearby group of nobles. They clustered around
a tall and powerful man who seemed to be speaking gravely.
But it was not the men who caught Rodrigo's eye. It was the
slim figure of a young girl standing next to them. Suddenly it
seemed to Rodrigo that all the color and brilliance of the gathering faded into gray beside the jet-black brilliance of her hair
and the soft luster of her cheeks. Rodrigo could not leave his
father's side, but he could not take his eyes away from the
beautiful young girl. As he accompanied don Diego through
the ranks of courtiers toward the throne, the unknown beauty
suddenly glanced up, as if aware that someone had been staring
at her. When her glance fell upon Rodrigo her face paled and
then her lips parted slightly in a smile. It was as if both Rodrigo
and the girl had suddenly recognized each other as old friends
—and much more.

"Father," Rodrigo whispered, "who is that girl?"

Don Diego followed Rodrigo's glance. "That is doña Jimena,
the daughter of the Count of Lozano, who is the tall man standing beside her. And if the count notices you staring at her he
will pay you his respects rather roughly, I fear."

The old man's words were interrupted suddenly by the shrill
blasting of trumpets. Rodrigo found himself standing with his
father in the front ranks of courtiers before the king. Fernando
rose to his feet, looked slowly at the great throng and gently
caressed his long white beard. Then he spoke.

"We, Fernando, King of Castille and Emperor of Leon, Overlord of Aragon and of Navarre, Tributary Lord of the Emirates

of Toledo and Zaragoza, declare that a great Council of State is now convened. We thank you for your attendance upon our wishes and we beseech the blessing of Almighty God upon this Council that we may be led to just and righteous solutions of the problems which afflict our realm."

The king seated himself and once again the trumpets sounded.

Now a herald stepped forward and from a great roll of parchment called out the names of all those present. As each name was called a noble would come forward, bend his knee to King Fernando and offer up his sword for service. The king would speak a few words and return the sword, and the next name would ring through the huge hall. When Rodrigo saw the priceless jewels, costly furs and golden weapons that the nobles presented as gifts to the king, he felt a sudden pang of shame that his father had brought only a parchment history of Castille.

"Don Diego de Vivar!"

Rodrigo found himself kneeling alongside his father before the king. The old scholar had presented his sword. The king gripped it firmly and handed it back. Then don Diego handed the king his parchment history. "Your Majesty, please accept this history of your Kingdom of Castille in testimony to the great love and esteem we bear you."

King Fernando accepted the book and smiled. "Don Diego, of all the gifts I have received this day, yours is the richest. You have given us the gift of your wisdom which is famous throughout our realm."

"Your Majesty does me honor!" don Diego replied proudly. "May I present to Your Majesty my eldest son, Rodrigo?"

The king's eyes turned to Rodrigo. "A fine young man, don Diego. He has the build of a warrior."

"I fear so, Your Majesty. He does not inherit my love of scholarship."

"Would you be a warrior, Rodrigo?" the king asked gravely.

"Yes, Your Majesty!" Rodrigo exclaimed. "I would be a knight to fight always in Your Majesty's cause!"

The king smiled. "You must prove yourself to be a knight." Then he frowned. "I fear there will soon be fighting enough in Castille."

Rodrigo hardly remembered how he and his father left that splendid hall. All that afternoon, while don Diego and some few of the king's closest advisors were gathered together in private council, Rodrigo spent his time in the royal stables, grooming *Pitiuso* and *Babieca,* while he pondered two problems. How was he to prove himself so that the king would knight him, and how was he to go about making the acquaintance of the beautiful Jimena?

It was later in the day, while Rodrigo sat on a stone bench outside the stable entrance still pondering these matters, when don Diego appeared. The old scholar's face was hard and his eyes flashed fire. Rodrigo had never seen his father so enraged.

"Father, what has happened?"

Don Diego's lips were tightly clenched but at last he spoke as if tearing the words from his heart. "I have been publicly insulted, before the king!"

Rodrigo stepped back, his hands clenching as if seeking weapons. "Who? Why?" were the only words he spoke.

"We were assembled in private council," don Diego said slowly. "The question before us was whether the king should divide his realm among his three sons when he dies, as has been our custom. I spoke up for the more ancient Gothic rule that the entire kingdom be inherited by the eldest son since that is our only hope against the Moors. But the great nobles prefer three weak kings to one strong one. Their spokesman was the Count of Lozano."

"But that is no insult, Father—"

"Hear me! The king made no decision regarding the inheritance. He will do that later. But he appointed me tutor to his three sons. It is a great honor. He said that if there must be three kings in Castille, he would have them brought up in wisdom. But the Count of Lozano had hoped to be appointed Royal Tutor himself. He and the other great nobles hope thus to influence the princes. The argument grew heated, I fear." Don Diego's voice sank away.

"And then?"

"Then, Rodrigo, the Count of Lozano said that I could only instruct the princes in cowardice. He slapped me twice across the face! If I were but a few years younger—"

Don Diego fell silent and the silence grew intense. Rodrigo realized that he must now make the acquaintance of the beautiful Jimena as the enemy of her father. For he knew his duty clearly.

"Father, you instructed me, and you did not teach me cowardice. Give me your sword!"

Don Diego smiled gravely. "You speak as I hoped you would." He unbuckled his sword and handed it to Rodrigo. "Take this sword, Rodrigo. It is named *Tizone*, and in my youth it was accustomed to avenging wrongs!"

Rodrigo took the sword, kissed his father on each cheek and then hurried to saddle *Babieca*. When he led the horse forth he asked, "Where will I find the Count of Lozano now, father?"

"He is quartered with his followers at the castle of Belares near the north gate of the city."

Rodrigo mounted and, without a backward look, spurred *Babieca* to a gallop.

It did not take him long to reach the castle of Belares. And as he rode into the great courtyard of the castle he saw the Count of Lozano, about to dismount from his horse.

"Who are you and what do you want?" the count demanded when he saw Rodrigo's warlike aspect.

26

"I am Rodrigo de Vivar. Do not dismount, count. I have come to take back the honor you stole from my father."

The count laughed. "Go away, young man! You are not even a knight, and yet you wish to cross swords with a man who is accustomed to victory! Depart while you may!"

"Then test me, count, to see whether I too can accustom myself to victory. Or do you only care to fight against the old and defenseless?"

"Leave me quickly, Rodrigo, before I lose my patience and give you the same blows I gave your father—or worse!"

"I see, count, that your patience makes you a coward!"

On hearing these words, the Count of Lozano, purple with rage, drew his sword and spurred his horse to charge against Rodrigo.

But Rodrigo had already guessed the count's intention. He parried the count's sword with *Tizone* and made *Babieca* turn quickly. Then, before the count had time to recover from his first charge, Rodrigo was upon him. *Tizone* struck sparks of fire from the count's sword while *Babieca* reared, wheeled and charged like a true war horse.

By this time many people had rushed from the castle to watch the fight and among them was Jimena. As she saw what was happening and recognized who battled against her father, her face paled and, as if some dreadful premonition had come to her, she could only whisper over and over, "No, please, God. No—"

Rodrigo and the count continued to fight, their swords clashing tirelessly, their horses' mouths flecked with foam. The count's experience was clearly matched by Rodrigo's youth and anger.

But when Rodrigo noticed Jimena's pallid face among the onlookers, he paused for a moment. "Count," he cried, "beg my father's pardon and we shall put an end to this quarrel!"

"I ask no pardon of cowards and villains! If you are afraid

then run away and tell your father he should be ashamed to have engendered such a cowardly son!"

Hearing these insults, Rodrigo forgot Jimena and attacked with such fury that the count found himself barely able to ward off the flashing blows of *Tizone*.

Standing up in *Babieca's* stirrups, his eyes fiery, and *Tizone* flashing on high, Rodrigo appeared to be an avenging angel. Soon he gave the count such a blow that the count's sword clattered from his hand. But *Tizone* cleft downward through shield and helmet and the count fell from his horse mortally wounded.

A cry of horror went up from the crowd of onlookers. Jimena, who had been praying that the fight might somehow end peacefully, fell fainting into the arms of her maid. And just at that

moment five royal heralds galloped into the castle courtyard. They saw quickly what had happened and rode over to Rodrigo.

"We had come, by His Majesty's command, to prevent what has already come to pass," one of them said. "Rodrigo de Vivar, you are ordered before the king!"

Rodrigo bowed his head, glanced for one anguished moment toward the portal through which Jimena had been carried and followed the heralds from the castle.

Rodrigo was brought into the king's presence in the great hall of Justice. But now the hall was empty save for guards and don Diego, who stood next to the king's throne. Rodrigo knelt to the king and then knelt before his father and presented *Tizone*. "Take back your sword, Father. With it I return to you the honor of which you were robbed."

Don Diego placed his hands on Rodrigo's shoulders and raised him up. "You shall keep this sword, my son. He who defends the honor of a family should be its head!"

King Fernando had watched all this in silence. Stroking his long white beard and with the faintest trace of a smile on his lips, he now spoke. "Rodrigo de Vivar, you have proved yourself in the test of battle worthy of being knighted. Kneel before me!"

Rodrigo knelt before the king.

Fernando touched Rodrigo's right shoulder with his sword. "Rodrigo de Vivar, do you wish to be a knight?" he demanded.

"Yes, Sire, I do!"

The king touched Rodrigo's left shoulder with his sword. "Rodrigo de Vivar, do you wish to be a knight?"

"Yes, Sire, I do!"

"Then, in the name of God and Santiago, I make you a knight! Be brave and loyal!" Then the king raised Rodrigo to his feet and embraced him as a brother.

"Your Majesty does me great honor!" Rodrigo exclaimed. He

could barely find words to express the tumult of emotions
within him.

The King seated himself upon his throne. "That may be,
Rodrigo," he said sternly. "But now we come to a grave matter.
In killing the Count of Lozano, even to avenge an insult, you
have committed a crime. The punishment for such a crime is
banishment. How say you?"

Rodrigo turned to his father. "Give me your benediction,
Father. I would not have it thought that my hand serves only
to avenge insults. For this reason I shall go forth to do battle
with the Moors!"

"You have proclaimed your own sentence, Rodrigo," the king
said. "We hereby banish you from all of our realms until it is
our pleasure to recall you. But we shall decide upon that only
when we have proofs of your loyalty and valor."

"I have heard and will obey, Sire!"

And with his father's blessing and *Tizone* buckled to his side,
Rodrigo hurried from the royal palace. He found *Babieca* waiting for him impatiently as if anxious to help his young master
prove himself on the field of battle for his king.

So it was that Rodrigo de Vivar in one afternoon had avenged
his family's honor, lost the love of doña Jimena, been knighted
by his king and banished from Castille. Now he rode forth from
the royal city of Burgos, one man with but one sword, to do
battle alone against the legions of the Moors.

How Rodrigo Won the Title
of El Cid Campeador

Although Rodrigo left the court of King Fernando, he did not immediately leave the kingdom. Instead he returned to Vivar to bid farewell to his mother. The news of his victory over the Count of Lozano and of his banishment preceded him. So when he reached his family's house, Rodrigo found several of the bravest and most adventurous of his boyhood friends waiting to follow him into exile.

"If you ride with me," Rodrigo warned them, "you are following one who is penniless and has incurred the anger of the king."

"With you to lead us, Rodrigo," they exclaimed, "we shall soon win riches enough from the Moors and the king's anger will be forgotten in his pride in our deeds."

A few hours later, with his mother's blessing, Rodrigo galloped forth from the town of Vivar followed by a band of *caballeros,* well armed with swords and lances, but better armed with faith and a desire for glory.

31

From that time forward hardly a day passed at the court of King Fernando that did not bring news of the heroic feats of Rodrigo de Vivar. Everyone spoke wonderingly of his bravery and his knightliness. One day would come notice of how Rodrigo and his little band had overcome a powerful group of bandits; another day would bring news of the defeat of some Moorish raiding party.

And it was not only among the Spaniards that Rodrigo's fame increased. Because of his bravery in battle he soon became feared and respected among the Moors.

One day as Rodrigo and his followers were riding through the desert lands on the border of the Moorish Emirate of Zaragoza, they beheld in the distance a rich convoy of heavily laden mules guarded by a mere handful of Moorish cavalry.

Touching his spurs to *Babieca's* flanks, Rodrigo led his companions in a charge that soon dispersed the Moorish guards and sent them fleeing across the desert. Then they wheeled their horses about and returned to see what spoils had fallen into their hands. They were met by several ancient Moorish merchants who instantly threw themselves onto the ground before Rodrigo's horse. The eldest of these merchants, pouring dust on his head and tugging on his long white beard, looked up at Rodrigo and said, "We know you for Rodrigo de Vivar, my Lord, and we know better than to offer you resistance. But this convoy contains a jewel of the greatest value intended for the Emir of Zaragoza. If we should lose it, our heads would be forfeit!"

When Rodrigo's companions heard this they smiled to think what a fortune must have fallen into their hands.

"Where is this jewel, merchant?" Rodrigo demanded.

The old man scrambled to his feet and walked over to the nearest mule. This animal, instead of bearing heavy sacks, carried on his back a small structure shaped like a miniature

mosque and completely covered with fine silks of many colors. "See for yourself, Rodrigo de Vivar!" the old merchant exclaimed as he drew back the silk curtains.

Sitting within was a young Moorish princess. Her lips trembled and tears ran down her cheeks. "This is the bride of the Emir of Zaragoza," the merchant declared, "and these other mules carry her dowry. She is to be wed within the week to the Emir." So saying he let fall the silk, again concealing the princess, and then threw himself once again on the ground before Rodrigo's horse.

Now Rodrigo's companions began to argue among themselves. "No mercy should be shown to Moors and infidels!" some of them exclaimed. "We should take the money and let the princess go," others said. "No, she will bring a great ransom from the Emir of Zaragoza!" still others argued.

All this time Rodrigo continued to stare at the silk-covered enclosure atop the mule. He could not help recalling how he was separated from his own love, the gentle Jimena. Finally he turned to his followers. "We must let them go unmolested," he declared. "Are we so poor that we would despoil a wedding party—even though it be Moorish?"

At this his companions fell silent. It was hard for them to forgo looting this rich convoy, but Rodrigo's words shamed them.

"Go on your way, merchant," Rodrigo said, "and give my best wishes to the Emir of Zaragoza on his wedding. Tell him, too, that he is a fool to entrust so precious a gem to so weak a guard!"

The old merchant struggled to his feet, his face wreathed in smiles. He called down the blessings of Allah upon Rodrigo and his men. But as he was speaking his lips faltered and he pointed with trembling fingers toward the nearby mountains.

There, in a cloud of dust, a large group of horsemen were charging down upon the convoy.

Rodrigo wheeled instantly and formed his men into a line of battle. He thought for a moment that Moorish cavalry had arrived. But as the horsemen drew nearer he saw that they were Castillians—bandits—to judge by their ragged appearance.

When the horsemen had come to within a hundred yards of the convoy they halted and one of their number, a gigantic man with a bright red beard who was mounted on a pure white Arabian charger, spurred forward to parley. Rodrigo advanced to meet him, his sword *Tizone* ready in his hand for any eventuality.

"Greetings, Rodrigo de Vivar!" the stranger called. "I see you have beaten us to the plunder!"

"Who are you?" Rodrigo demanded.

The huge ragged stranger grinned. "I am Gonzalvo de Los Sierras. You should know me by my beard!"

A wail went up from the Moorish merchants behind Rodrigo as they recognized the name of the most fearsome bandit in all of Spain.

"This convoy is under my protection," Rodrigo said.

Gonzalvo shrugged, his eyes agleam as they glanced at the heavily laden mules. "That may be," he said, "but you see that my men outnumber yours three to one. Still, if we were to fight over these spoils we would only be hurting each other. Why should we not put these Moorish dogs to death and divide the booty equally?"

"I have given my word that this convoy is not to be touched," Rodrigo said quietly. But as he spoke he was thinking quickly. It was true that if they fought, his men would almost certainly lose the battle against such odds. If only he could force Gonzalvo to fight him alone. "But since it is my personal word,

35

Gonzalvo," he said, "perhaps you would not be afraid to settle the matter personally in single combat?"

Gonzalvo de Los Sierras grinned and spat into the dirt before *Babieca*. "Why should I agree to that? My men and I can take all this for ourselves with very little trouble."

"Perhaps, then, you are afraid to fight me, Gonzalvo?" Rodrigo demanded loudly. He hoped to shame the bandit before his own men and thus force him to fight.

Gonzalvo leaned back his head and roared with laughter. "We bandits have no shame!" he cried. "Know that I have defeated more than one hundred knights in personal combat. A child like you I would eat for breakfast! But I make no bargains and no agreements."

Rodrigo glanced behind him and saw that his men, with lowered lances and drawn swords, were prepared to die for him. But he knew also that they faced certain defeat. So, riding up close to Gonzalvo he suddenly reached out and plucked a hair from the bandit's heavy red beard. He raised the hair on high and shouted to Gonzalvo's followers, "See the hair I pluck from the beard of your cowardly leader! You should be ashamed to follow such a one!"

Now plucking a hair from a man's beard was the gravest insult that could be offered in those days. Gonzalvo's face turned red with fury. Forgetting his greed, he gave himself up to rage. Without another word, he dealt Rodrigo such a blow that *Tizone* went spinning out of his hand and into the dust.

Rodrigo's men groaned aloud when they saw that he now faced certain death, while Gonzalvo's thieves laughed and cheered.

Rodrigo knew it would be but a matter of seconds before this gigantic bandit killed him. Spurring *Babieca*, he wheeled suddenly behind Gonzalvo and sprang from his saddle, dragging the bandit down to the ground with him. There they rolled and struggled desperately, Rodrigo trying to wrest Gonzalvo's sword from him. A deep silence spread around them in which only their own heavy breathing and muffled groans could be heard. Then suddenly the bandit's sword went flying through the air to land in the dirt next to *Tizone*. But at the same moment Gonzalvo was on his feet, a dagger glinting in his hand as he sprang upon Rodrigo. Rodrigo rolled to escape the blow, jumped to his feet and raced Gonzalvo to the place where both their swords lay. He snatched up *Tizone* and turned to face his enemy.

"Very well, Rodrigo de Vivar," Gonzalvo gasped, "as you now have a sword and I have none, you may kill me. I will never yield!"

37

"For your treacherous attack I would be justified in killing you like a dog!" Rodrigo cried. "But take up your sword and fight like a man, if you claim to be one!" So saying he tossed Gonzalvo's sword to him.

Now the two enemies circled each other warily, swords in hand, each trying to judge the time and place for a decisive blow. Suddenly Rodrigo made a thrust at Gonzalvo's chest, purposely exposing his flank to do so. Gonzalvo uttered a cheer, sidestepped Rodrigo's thrust and swung his sword in a vicious arc toward Rodrigo's exposed side. His blade met nothing but air as Rodrigo, recovering from his feint, sidestepped and brought *Tizone* whistling through the air to deal his off-balance enemy a mortal blow.

Rodrigo's followers cheered when they saw Gonzalvo fall dead, though they held themselves ready for any new treachery. But the bandits, seeing their leader killed, turned tail suddenly and sped away across the desert as if pursued by demons.

Now the Moorish merchants clustered around Rodrigo, helping him back onto *Babieca* and praising him for his valor. They called him *"El mio Cid, Campeador,"* which meant "My Lord, the Champion." And when they offered Rodrigo and his men half of all the treasure that was intended for the Emir's wedding dowry, Rodrigo refused. "My word," he said, "means more to me than all the treasures in Spain. Go in peace."

"Allah bless you, *Campeador!*" the eldest merchant exclaimed, "In a good hour were you born!"

From that time forth Rodrigo's renown among the Moors increased until his title *El Mio Cid, Campeador,* had spread throughout all of Spain.

Now while Rodrigo was winning glory for himself among the Moors, King Fernando was faced by a vexing problem. The Emirate of Zaragoza paid him a rich tribute each year for his protection. But since Zaragoza was completely surrounded by Christian kingdoms, it was not unusual for one of them to seize part of the Emir's territory. The King of Aragon had taken a few of the Emir's villages, and it was King Fernando's duty to defend the Emir, even though it meant spilling Christian blood to defend the rights of Moors.

One day as the old king was considering this problem in the company of Rodrigo's father, a soldier entered the council chamber to announce the arrival of an ambassador from the King of Aragon.

"Let him be brought before us immediately," Fernando commanded. He picked up his jeweled sword of state and seated himself on his throne. Don Diego stood next to him.

The ambassador from the King of Aragon proved to be don Martín González, a very famous knight. Once in the royal presence, don Martín bent his knee and said, "Your Majesty, it is shameful for Aragon and Castille to shed Christian blood for the sake of a few poor Moorish villages."

"You are right, don Martín," Fernando replied. "These villages are not worth battling over. But they must be returned to the Emir."

"My king, don Ramiro has sworn to keep them," don Martín said. "But to avoid a battle, I have come in the name of my king to beg you to appoint a champion who will fight me in single combat. He who wins the fight wins also these villages for his king."

"You may tell don Ramiro," Fernando said after a moment's thought, "that we will soon choose a knight to fight in the name of Castille."

No sooner had don Martín left the council chamber than don Diego bent his knee to the king and said, "Your Majesty, I know there are many Castillian knights who would feel themselves honored to fight in your name. But I beg you for the sake of my services to you, to give my son Rodrigo this opportunity to defend you and Castille."

"I had already thought of him," Fernando replied. "But although I have in my heart already pardoned him for the death of Count Lozano, I do not think it would be well thought of in my court."

"Sire, you know very well that there is no one better fitted to win the victory for Castille," don Diego insisted.

The king thought deeply for a few minutes and then said, "Very well, it shall be Rodrigo. And you may inform him for me that I hope he will come to tell me of his victory in person."

"Thank you, Sire," don Diego said.

That same afternoon a royal messenger left Burgos in search of Rodrigo, bearing the good news that if he could win this victory in the name of Castille, he might return to the royal court, his banishment at an end.

Rodrigo's joy was very great when he heard of the mission with which he was honored. He immediately ordered his followers to strike their tents, and, avoiding all encounters with the Moors, they took the road to Aragon.

When Rodrigo arrived at the royal court of Aragon he presented his credentials as the champion of Castille and was introduced to don Martín González, against whom he would have to fight.

"Are you the man who is called The Cid by a few cowardly Moors?" don Martín asked him contemptuously.

"I am," Rodrigo replied calmly.

"And are you not aware of my fame?"

"I have heard something about you," Rodrigo said. "But I know of many men whose fame exists only in words."

"You are very arrogant, young man!" don Martín cried. "You will soon have an opportunity of judging whether my fame exists in words or deeds!"

"I am anxious then to fight with you. It will be a great honor to have defeated so famous a knight," Rodrigo said.

According to the ancient rules, this single combat had to take place on the border between Aragon and Castille. There the judges from both sides met to arrange the fight. Five hundred soldiers accompanied each of the knights and, when they reached the appointed spot, formed themselves into ranks behind their respective champions.

The Cid waited patiently, mounted on *Babieca*, whose saddle and reins had been polished until they shone like glass. On his left arm he bore a shield decorated with a scarlet dragon. In his right hand he balanced a lance which rested on the crupper of his saddle, and in his belt hung *Tizone*, the invincible sword, gleaming brightly in the sunlight. When his companions offered him advice Rodrigo listened with a silent smile.

Suddenly the trumpets sounded and The Cid spurred *Babieca* forward to meet don Martín's charge. The two horses gathered speed quickly and when they met the shock was terrific. Don Martín's lance, crashing into The Cid's shield, splintered and flew into the air, while Rodrigo's lance accidentally pierced the armor of don Martín's horse and was torn from his hand as the animal went down. The Cid immediately descended from *Babieca*, drew his sword and waited for don Martín to disentangle himself from his dying horse. The Castillian judges now claimed the victory for The Cid, according to the rules. But Rodrigo, by a sign of his hand, let them understand that he wished to complete his triumph.

Don Martín's humiliation at having taken a fall at the hands of The Cid was so great that he now threw himself forward like a crazy man, his sword striking great sparks from Rodrigo's shield and helmet. The Cid returned blow for blow. "You see now, don Martín," he cried, "I am not fighting against Moors!"

Don Martín fought like a lion, but his shield slowly went to pieces under the terrible blows of *Tizone*. Seeing that he must soon lose the battle, he threw himself with desperate courage upon The Cid. But Rodrigo, with a quick step, avoided the rush and gave don Martín one final and terrible blow. *Tizone* cut through shield and armor to leave the Champion of Aragon dying upon the field.

A great shout went up among the soldiers of Castille when they saw that their champion had won the day. The judges and all the witnesses proclaimed The Cid victorious. And while don Martín's body was being carried away on his shield, Rodrigo and his men turned their horses toward Burgos to rush the joyous news to King Fernando. Rodrigo paid little attention to the praises and congratulations of his men. What mattered most to him was that at long last, after many dangers, he was able to return in honor to his own land and to doña Jimena.

But while The Cid was fighting in Aragon there had been some who spoke against him at the court of King Fernando. These people were jealous of The Cid's growing fame. To harm him they tried to persuade doña Jimena to demand justice from the king for the death of her father. But in these matters, don Sancho, King Fernando's eldest son, proved himself a true friend of The Cid.

"How is it, doña Jimena," he asked, "that you would seek vengeance against a man who loves you?"

Doña Jimena, confused and tearful, replied, "To take vengeance for an offense against his father, Rodrigo was willing to leave me in the greatest sorrow."

"It was his duty to avenge his father," Prince Sancho pointed out.

"And it is my duty to avenge mine," doña Jimena said, her voice full of misery.

Soon afterward the sad young girl presented herself before King Fernando. "Sire," she begged, "do me justice. As a woman I cannot punish the man who killed my father."

King Fernando put his arm around Jimena and said, "You know, Jimena, that Rodrigo has already fulfilled his punishment, being exiled from his own country."

"But I know that you have honored him to fight against Aragon in your own name."

"That is true," the king declared, "but probably at this very moment Rodrigo is dead, because his enemy is the greatest and bravest of all the knights of Aragon."

On hearing these words, doña Jimena burst into tears.

"But in any case," King Fernando said comfortingly, "you have fulfilled your duty as a daughter in trying to avenge the death of your father. Now try to save your love."

At that moment a messenger entered the room and whispered a few words into the king's ear.

"Jimena," King Fernando said, "listen to the news this messenger brings. At this very moment Rodrigo is waiting outside the city gates. He has returned victorious from Aragon and asks permission to present himself before us. Although I authorized him to return, I now wish that you would decide. What say you?"

Jimena, on hearing these words, could not conceal her pleasure. But she continued to feign indifference. "Let it be as Your Majesty decides," she said.

King Fernando smiled. "In that case I decide in favor of Rodrigo," he said. "Let the Champion of Castille be brought before us!"

To the sound of trumpets and the cheers of the royal court, Rodrigo and his men presented themselves before the king. Kneeling before Fernando, The Cid said, "Your Majesty, in your name I have won the victory for Castille."

The king ordered Rodrigo to his feet. Then, embracing him as a son, he said, "In the name of Castille we give you thanks and pray that God will reward your valor!"

Rodrigo bowed again to the king and tried to depart. But at that moment Prince Sancho came up to him, greeting him gaily and congratulating him on his victory. Soon all the court surrounded The Cid, each trying to outdo the others in praise and flattery. But Prince Sancho drew Rodrigo apart from the crowd to where doña Jimena was standing, alone. Her face plainly reflected the confusion of her feelings. She was not able to hate and love at the same time.

"Doña Jimena," The Cid said with deep humility, "I beg your pardon. I have paid for my faults with wounds."

Before this gallant and humble apology, it was love which won in doña Jimena's heart. Smiling, she raised her hand for Rodrigo to kiss. He did so, and from the depths of his heart said, "Doña Jimena, may God bless you for the charity you show me."

In the following weeks Rodrigo was kept very busy by the activities of the court. He went hunting and hawking with Prince Sancho, who had become his best friend, paid court to the lovely Jimena, and listened patiently to the lengthy speeches of his father on such matters as philosophy, astrology and politics. He was also required to attend to the presence of the king, who showed him every sign of respect and affection.

One day as old don Diego was lecturing Rodrigo in the principles of heraldry, the lesson was interrupted by a messenger who ordered both father and son to attend the king in the great Council Chamber. When they arrived they found all the principal nobles and advisors of the court gathered. Also present were the king's three sons, don Sancho, don Alfonso and don García, as well as his daughter, doña Urraca. From the expression of deep gravity upon King Fernando's face they realized that he was about to make an important announcement.

With all his court gathered about him, King Fernando rose from his throne, gripping his great sword of state. "Nobles and counselors of the realm!" he proclaimed. "We are full of years and would spend what little time that remains to us in ordering our spiritual affairs before we go to meet our God. For this reason we have decided to abdicate our throne and divide our kingdom amongst our sons. To don Sancho, our first born, we grant the Kingdom of Castille and all its tributaries. To don Alfonso, our second son, we give the Kingdom of León and the overlordship of the Moorish kingdom of Toledo, and to don García, the youngest of our sons, we grant the Kingdom of Galicia and the tributes due from the Moorish Emirs of Seville and Badajoz. To our daughter Urraca is granted the city of Zamora. May each of them hold their kingdoms in peace. And we especially beg our loyal subjects don Diego de Vivar and his son Rodrigo to counsel our sons wisely and defend them always."

"Sire," don Diego said as he bent his knee, "it is a difficult mission you entrust to me and my son. But we swear to follow your wishes." Rodrigo knelt with his father and swore also.

King Fernando continued then, advising his sons to respect each other's inheritances and to keep them in peace always and to abide by the wishes of God.

And so King Fernando retired from his throne after reigning for many years in justice and honor. He went to a monastery to devote himself to holy duties and meditations. And while he continued alive his three sons respected his wishes and remained, each in their own kingdoms, at peace with each other.

As soon as Prince Sancho had been proclaimed King of Castille, he called Rodrigo before him and named him Commander-in-Chief of all his armies. This was a title of great honor which Rodrigo gratefully accepted. But it was also a title of great danger. For in those days the Commander-in-Chief of the royal army was expected to fight in single combat whenever necessary as the champion of the king. And since kings had many quarrels in those days, very few Commanders-in-Chief remained more than a few years in that position.

It was not long before a dispute arose between the Kingdoms of Castille and Navarre. It concerned the possession of the strong frontier castle of Pazuengos. King Sancho sent The Cid as his ambassador to the King of Navarre, telling him to preserve peace if he could, but to uphold the rights and honor of Castille in any case.

When The Cid was presented to the King of Navarre, he said, "I have come, Your Majesty, to reclaim in the name of Castille the fortress you have seized from us unlawfully."

"Pazuengos is rightfully part of the territory of Navarre," the King of Navarre replied. "I have taken that fortress by force of arms and only by force of arms will it be taken from me."

"But those lands are part of Castille," Rodrigo objected. "It would be better, Sire, to see them returned to their rightful owner than to see bloody war between Navarre and Castille."

The Navarrese king, understanding the veiled threat behind Rodrigo's words, and considering the power of the army of Castille, turned to consult a few moments with his advisors. Then he said to The Cid: "In order to preserve peace between our two kingdoms, we will agree to submit this quarrel to the justice of God."

The Cid understood then that he would have to fight in single combat as the champion of Castille. But he thought this a thousand times better than a cruel and costly war. "Let the justice of God be done, Sire," he said.

Now in the court of Navarre in those days, the great champion was Jimeno Garcés. His strength and skill as a knight were famous throughout Spain; he counted his victories by the hundreds. It was for this reason that the King of Navarre had elected to submit his quarrel to personal combat. He had every confidence that Jimeno Garcés would easily win.

When The Cid learned who his opponent was to be he was very sad. He had known Jimeno Garcés for several years and he knew him to be an upright and courteous knight. If there had been any way to avoid this fight, with honor, The Cid would willingly have done so. But his word was given to King Sancho of Castille and he had accepted the decision of the King of Navarre. And so, on the following day, Rodrigo and Jimeno Garcés met in mortal combat on a field near the border between Navarre and Castille. The fight was furious but very short. With his first charge The Cid's lance toppled Jimeno Garcés from his horse. Rodrigo would then have gladly offered mercy to his opponent, but Jimeno Garcés' humiliation was too great. "To win the castle of Pazuengos from my royal master you must kill me first, Cid!" he cried, and drew his sword. The Cid dismounted from *Babieca,* drew *Tizone* from its jeweled scabbard, and within a few moments the sound of steel ringing on steel was at an end. With one mighty stroke The Cid had slain Jimeno Garcés.

But as he left the field, with the cheers ringing in his ears, Rodrigo's heart was heavy. Once again he had settled a dispute between his king and another. But to accomplish this he had been forced to kill a very great knight. "Instead of killing each other," he mused, "would it not be better to band together and drive the Moors from our common homeland? Why should Spaniards spill their blood against each other in these petty feuds when we need all our strength to defeat a common enemy?"

Full of such thoughts, The Cid returned to Burgos, where he was received in great honor and with much rejoicing. After reporting his victory to King Sancho and courteously greeting his father and doña Jimena, Rodrigo retired to the royal chapel. There he meditated and prayed to God to grant him the chance to unite the Spanish kingdoms and lead them against the Moors. The problems were very great and The Cid did not then see how he could accomplish this task. But from that day forward he was a consecrated man.

How The Cid Made Castille Supreme in Spain and Yet Was Banished

If The Cid now dreamed of uniting all of Spanish Christendom peacefully, the young King Sancho, his royal master, had ambitions of doing so through war. Sancho had never forgotten that as the first born of King Fernando he should have inherited all of his father's kingdoms. When, one day, news was brought of the old king's death at his monastery, Sancho felt himself free to act. After the period of mourning was concluded he called The Cid to his side.

"Rodrigo," he said, "since my father is dead, I am free now to assert my just claim to the kingdoms of León and Galicia."

"But your father left those kingdoms to your brothers, Your Majesty," Rodrigo replied.

Sancho shrugged and stared pensively at the sword of state that rested across his knees. "My father, of blessed memory, was in poor health when he made that decision. Had he been of a whole mind he would have assigned all his lands to me. Besides, Rodrigo, you have lately been saying that you want to see all of Christian Spain united, haven't you?"

"Peacefully, Your Majesty."

"And so it shall be, if possible. But your first duty in any event is to your sovereign."

The Cid bowed his head and spoke no further. Here was a problem indeed! He had sworn to protect all of King Fernando's sons. And now, to defend one he must war against another. He had also sworn to unite Spain. But now he would be warring against Spaniards. He sought out his father for advice.

Don Diego had grown very old and frail in the past years. When he heard Rodrigo's problem he pulled his bearskin rug over his lap, stroked his white beard thoughtfully and finally declared, "Spain will never be united peacefully, Rodrigo. But King Sancho is very ambitious. He will probably succeed in conquering his brothers' kingdoms. If you remain beside him you will at least be able to prevent unnecessary bloodshed, and perhaps one day you will be able to keep your vow to God to lead Christian Spain against the Moors. I have small hope of living to see that day, yet I would die more content if I thought you had kept your vow to God."

A few days later King Sancho sent a letter to his brother Alfonso asking that Alfonso turn over his Kingdom of León in return for certain rents and privileges. But King Alfonso, encouraged by the counsel of his advisors, haughtily refused. Three months later war broke out between Castille and León.

When he heard of this tragic news, The Cid presented himself immediately before King Sancho. "Grant me dispensation, Sire, not to fight against your brother King Alfonso. My sword is powerful only against Moors, not Christians."

"It is for the unity of Christian Spain that we shall be fighting, Rodrigo," King Sancho replied.

"Allow me at least, Your Majesty, to try to reach some agreement with King Alfonso in order to prevent useless bloodshed."

And so it came about that The Cid met with King Alfonso of León on a field named Llantada, between both the royal armies. The Cid convinced King Alfonso to agree that this one battle should be decisive. Whoever emerged victorious would rule both Castille and León.

Nevertheless, although The Cid and King Sancho led their army in such a furious charge and with such courage that they quickly put the troops of León to flight, King Alfonso ran away to the fortified city of León, shut himself up within the walls and refused to abide by his agreement.

Since King Sancho's forces were not strong enough to besiege the city of León, he was forced to retire from the field with an empty victory.

In the months that followed, through the constant efforts of The Cid, King Sancho and King Alfonso established a peace between themselves. But The Cid was surprised and mortified to find that these two kings now turned their combined forces against their youngest brother, Garcia, and, through threats, forced him to yield up his Kingdom of Galicia without a battle. Galicia was now divided between Castille and León.

But the alliance between King Sancho and King Alfonso did not survive long. A few months after they had divided Galicia between them, the old quarrel about the battle of Llantada broke out afresh. Once again The Cid, much against his wishes, was forced to arrange a single battle between the two armies in order to spare some bloodshed at least. King Alfonso decided to fight this battle near the walled city of Santa Maria de Carrión.

The night before the battle, surrounded by his sleeping army, King Sancho talked with his nobles. He knew that the army of León was larger than his own and he hoped to encourage his knights. "They may be numerous," King Sancho declared, "but we are better and stronger. My lance alone will account for one thousand of their best knights and the lance of Rodrigo will kill at least one hundred of them."

"For myself," The Cid commented, "I can only say that I will fight as well as I can against one knight at a time, and God will decide in every case."

"Oh, Rodrigo," King Sancho exclaimed, "admit that you will kill at least fifty—well, then, forty—thirty—twenty—ten—" The king continued to press his champion, but unsuccessfully.

"I can fight against only one knight at a time, and God will decide," The Cid insisted, despite the promptings of his king.

It was just at dawn that the army of León attacked the Castillian camp, taking it entirely by surprise. The shock was terrible and the bloodshed very great. The troops of King Sancho, barely able to defend themselves, fled in terror, each man trying to save himself as best he might.

The Cid tried desperately to rally the army. Riding *Babieca,* his shield battered by hundreds of blows, his lance long since shattered, but with *Tizone* waving on high, he held back much of the Leónese army single-handed. But it was to no avail. The strategy of King Alfonso had been subtle and daring and the field was his. Worse than that, fourteen of Alfonso's best knights, making a daring dash right through the disorganized ranks of Castille, seized King Sancho and led him away a prisoner.

When The Cid saw his king being led from the field of battle by the enemy he uttered a terrible cry and galloped over to them. "Where are you taking my king?" he demanded. "Release him at once!"

"Do you expect to rescue him single-handed?" the Leónese knights shouted amid much laughter.

"Give me a lance, cowards, and you will see that I alone am more than enough to rescue my king!" Rodrigo cried. He hoped to excite their pride, and he succeeded.

The Leónese knights, instead of hurrying their most valuable prisoner from the field, contemptuously stuck a lance into the ground and turned to mock The Cid.

Spurring *Babieca* to a gallop, Rodrigo grabbed up the lance on the charge, brought it up to his crupper and killed one of the Leónese knights in the same rush. Then, before the others had time to form a line of battle, The Cid charged them with the fury of a demon, wounding and slaying on all sides. He reached the side of King Sancho, armed him with a sword taken from a dead Leónese, and together they continued to fight with terrible fury. It was not long before most of the fourteen knights were dead and the rest had fled, covered with wounds.

"Many thanks, my good Rodrigo," King Sancho gasped. "I shall never be able to repay you for what you have done this day."

"I have done only my duty, and God has granted us good fortune," Rodrigo replied.

King Alfonso had ordered his army not to pursue the Castillians, because he thought that after their defeat and the capture of their king, he had reason enough to claim the victory and therefore the two crowns of León and Castille. But when he learned how King Sancho had been rescued he was enraged and heaped curses on the head of The Cid.

Rodrigo, meanwhile, making use of the moonless night that now masked the field, reunited his scattered troops and raised their fallen spirits. Arranging what remained of them into a powerful wedge with himself at the head, he led them now in a charge through the darkness upon the army of León.

King Alfonso and his men, thinking that the battle was over, were carelessly feasting and celebrating their victory when suddenly The Cid and the desperate army of Castille burst upon them. It seemed to the Leónese that the gates of Hades had been opened to loose this horde of furious horsemen into their

midst. Without time to mount their horses or even to draw their swords, they were quickly defeated.

King Alfonso himself was barely able to escape from his tent and take refuge in the nearby walled town of Santa Maria de Carrión. But The Cid followed him there, made him prisoner and carried him off to his capital, the royal city of León. There King Alfonso gave over his crown to King Sancho of Castille and, accompanied by the family Beni-Gomez, went into exile at the court of the Moorish King El-Mamun in the city of Toledo. This terrible defeat on the fields of Carrión was a thing that neither Alfonso nor the family Beni-Gomez would ever forget or forgive. In later years The Cid was to pay heavily for his hard-won victory.

Now that King Sancho had won the crowns of León and Galicia, he ruled all the lands which had been his father's, with a single exception. This was the walled city of Zamora, which Fernando had granted to his daughter, Urraca. It was not a very important inheritance, but the city itself was strong, and King Sancho suspected his sister of plotting against him. It was true that all of King Sancho's enemies found refuge there.

Once again The Cid was forced to act the part of ambassador by King Sancho. It was a task he found very disagreeable, since he had known Queen Urraca for many years during the·time of her father, King Fernando.

Rodrigo was received very courteously by Queen Urraca in Zamora. He announced the reason for his visit with great embarrassment. "Your brother, King Sancho, has sent me to ask you to give him up the city of Zamora in return for riches and honors."

"And is it you, my good Rodrigo, the friend of my childhood, who comes now to ask me to renounce my inheritance?" the queen demanded.

"Perhaps, after all, Your Majesty, it would be better if all the Christian Kingdoms of Spain were united beneath one hand," Rodrigo answered evasively.

"And I always counted upon you as a friend, Rodrigo!"

"And I always will be," The Cid interrupted. "But I beg you to remember that at this moment I am no more than an ambassador from your brother and my king."

"Since you have so much influence with him," said the queen, "intercede for me and beg him to respect the wishes of our beloved father, King Fernando."

"Although I have no hope of persuading him, my Lady, I will try, I promise you."

"In any case," the queen continued, "I cannot make such a decision alone. I must consult my nobles."

"Then I beg you to consult them, Your Majesty, so that I can bring an answer to King Sancho."

But when Queen Urraca met with her nobles they decided unanimously to defend Zamora and resist the pretensions of King Sancho.

Upon hearing this decision The Cid said to Queen Urraca, "Please know, Your Majesty, that it is not against yourself that the king complains, but against the fact that your city has become the refuge of all his enemies and the place where treasons are continually plotted against him." Then, courteously saluting all those present, Rodrigo took his leave and returned to Castille.

When King Sancho heard that his sister and her nobles were determined to defend Zamora he became very angry. The Cid observed that ambition had changed Sancho from the honest young prince he had sworn to serve into a grasping and impatient monarch. But The Cid's oath had been taken before his king and his God and he could never break it. When old don Diego heard of this new war it was a final blow. He declined rapidly and died one evening in Rodrigo's arms. His last words adjured Rodrigo to remain faithful to his king and to keep his vow before God.

Several weeks later, in spite of The Cid's earnest advice and pleadings, King Sancho assembled his army and marched against the city of Zamora. There he surrounded the strong walls of the city with divisions of infantry and mounted knights and brought forth siege engines to tear down the fortifications. The Castillians attacked with great courage, advancing with shields raised over their heads to protect themselves against the clouds of arrows the defenders poured down upon them. They brought scaling ladders also to mount the ramparts. But, because the city was very strong, and possibly because The Cid's heart was not in this battle, King Sancho's army found that they could not carry the city by storm. So they settled down to starve out the defenders.

Within Zamora the situation soon grew desperate. The queen and her nobles knew that without food they would quickly be forced to surrender. Unbeknownst to Queen Urraca, some of her nobles now conceived of a desperate plan.

One dark and stormy night, King Sancho, accompanied by The Cid and by twenty knights who formed his bodyguard, was riding close by the walls of the sleeping city. He wanted to see with his own eyes what effect his siege engines had upon the fortifications. Suddenly they were surprised by a loud sound of shouting and clashing of arms from the nearest tower. Amid the shadows they saw a man jump desperately from the parapet of the tower and flee toward them, followed by a hail of arrows.

The king and his followers soon caught this fugitive and made him prisoner. "Who are you and why do you flee from Zamora?" King Sancho demanded.

The prisoner replied, "My name is Bellido Dolfos, Sire, and I have fled that accursed city because they wanted to kill me."

"And why did they want to kill you?" King Sancho asked.

"Because I said that Zamora could no longer resist and that it would be better to surrender now than to die of hunger and without hope of salvation."

The Cid sensed something false in the prisoner's words. Turning to King Sancho he said, "Your Majesty, let me find out if all this man says be true."

"This man does not lie," the king replied impatiently. "Did you not see how they shot a cloud of arrows after him?"

Seeing that King Sancho was angered by his interference, The Cid said no more.

Turning to Bellido Dolfos, King Sancho said, "Come with me. I want you to tell me the true situation of the defenders of Zamora."

Once within the royal tent, the fugitive told at great length how starvation and hopelessness reigned within the city. He told also of a place in the wall where some of King Sancho's men, taking advantage of a dark night, might slip in, easily overpower the tired and hungry guards and then lower the drawbridge for the rest of the Castillians to follow.

King Sancho grew very excited when he heard this news and arranged that the next day the fugitive should lead him to where he could see this entrance.

So the following morning, escorted by The Cid and twenty knights, King Sancho accompanied Bellido Dolfos to a part of the forest that grew near the walls of Zamora. But when they came close, the fugitive pointed to a high tree on the edge of the woods near the wall. "From that tree, Your Majesty, you can see the place I told you about."

"Let us go at once to see it!" the king cried impulsively.

"My Lord," Bellido Dolfos said, "it would be better if we went one by one, for if we go all together, we will be seen from the walls and they will guess our purpose."

"In that case you and I shall go first," King Sancho said impatiently.

Since Bellido Dolfos was completely unarmed and King Sancho carried both a sword in his belt and a short spear in his hand, and since the tree was no great distance from where they waited, The Cid and the royal bodyguard made no objection to this plan.

King Sancho and Bellido Dolfos, carefully hiding among the trees, made their way slowly to the edge of the forest where it fronted on the city. At last they came to the tree pointed out earlier by Dolfos. "If Your Majesty will climb to the first branch of this tree, you will see the opening in the wall of which I spoke," the fugitive whispered.

King Sancho rested his spear against the trunk of the tree in order to climb with more ease. He had just reached the first limb and was peering intently toward the wall when Bellido Dolfos seized the spear and plunged it into the king's back, shouting, "Die, ambitious king!"

The Cid, as soon as he saw Dolfos grab the spear, had shouted out a warning to the king. But his warning came too late, and the fugitive, having mortally wounded King Sancho, fled to the walls of the city. The Cid charged after him, *Tizone* raised on high, ignoring a rain of arrows that came down upon him from the city walls. But Bellido Dolfos was too close to the walls and he made his way safely into the city through a gate that had been opened for him.

The Cid, overcome with rage and grief, raced back to the royal tent where the wounded king had been carried. Surrounded by his nobles and knights, all grieving openly, King Sancho now looked his last upon his boyhood friend. "Rodrigo," he gasped, "beg pardon for me from my brothers and sister for all the harm I have done them. And you, knights and nobles, bear testimony that I commend my loyal friend and great

champion, Rodrigo Diaz de Vivar, to my brother, King Alfonso."
So saying, the king breathed his last, in the arms of his faithful
Commander-in-Chief.

Upon the death of the king, the army of Castille retired from
the siege of Zamora and sorrowfully bore the body of their
monarch back to Burgos. All the land was plunged into the
deepest mourning. Many nobles and even commoners whispered that King Sancho had been thus treacherously murdered
at the urging of his brother, King Alfonso.

Alfonso, after the terrible defeat on the plains of Carrión,
had sought refuge with his advisors, the family Beni-Gomez, in
the Moorish city of Toledo. Now he had suddenly inherited all
of his brother's dominions. He was king of Castille, León and

Galicia. Thus The Cid's efforts to unite Christian Spain had fallen into the hands of a king who had been his sworn enemy in the past.

Rodrigo thought deeply about this change of kings. He spoke to his cousin Alvar Hañez, a famous knight. "You know, Alvar, of how I swore to old King Fernando to defend all of his three sons."

Alvar Hañez frowned and examined the edge of his sword. The two knights were standing alone in the deserted Council Chamber of the palace at Burgos. "I remember, Rodrigo. But you have been unlucky enough to twice defeat Alfonso in battle. He is not likely to forgive that. And his advisors, these Beni-Gomez, they have long and cruel memories. Times are changing in Castille. If I were you I would see to my personal fortunes and hasten to make doña Jimena my wife."

"I must first fulfill one last duty to the memory of King Sancho," The Cid replied.

"And what is that?"

"I must have Alfonso's sworn word that he had no part in the assassination of his brother."

Alvar Hañez returned his sword to his scabbard. "I was afraid of that," he sighed. "You will certainly make him your enemy if you disgrace him publicly, Rodrigo. And what is there to prevent him from lying, anyhow?"

"He will swear before God," Rodrigo replied. "If he lies it shall be upon his soul." He drew *Tizone* from its scabbard and stared thoughtfully at its jeweled handle. "I long ago dedicated this word to the service of King Sancho. If Alfonso be innocent I shall dedicate it to him, too. But if he be guilty of this murder, *Tizone* will never rest in its scabbard again until he has paid for it!"

Alvar Hañez said no more. He knew it was impossible to dissuade his cousin.

Not many days later, attended by a large train of nobles,

Alfonso left Toledo and made his way toward Burgos to be crowned King of Castille. He was met at the border by The Cid and the assembled nobles of Castille. "Your Majesty," The Cid proclaimed, "here you see the nobles of Castille. They have come to greet you as their new king. But though none of them would speak of it, there are many throughout this kingdom who suspect you of having caused the murder of your brother, King Sancho. For this reason I must tell you that unless you take a solemn oath that this is not true, I, for one, will never kiss your hand or receive you as my king."

King Alfonso was greatly surprised to hear these words. But he understood that if he refused The Cid's request he would plunge his entire kingdom into civil war. So he answered; "I promise to take this oath in whatever form is desired by the nobility of Castille."

After consulting with his knights, The Cid returned. "Your Majesty will have to swear in the Church of Santa Gadea along with twelve of your knights."

To this King Alfonso agreed.

The very next day, in the royal city of Burgos, within the walls of the church of Santa Gadea, King Alfonso and his twelve knights, surrounded by all the glittering nobility of Castille and León, beneath the silken banners of the kingdom and with their hands upon the Bible, swore a solemn oath.

The Cid, his armor sparkling in the reflected light of thousands of candles, advanced toward King Alfonso and spoke.

"King Alfonso! Before you are crowned King of Castille, swear before God that the death of your brother, King Sancho was neither by your advice nor your order!"

"Yes, we swear to it," replied Alfonso and all of his twelve knights.

"If you lie, may God send you death like that suffered by King Sancho!"

"Amen," King Alfonso and his knights replied to this curse.

63

Three times The Cid made King Alfonso swear. The third time he presented his sword to the new king and respectfully kissed his hand.

Alfonso then returned *Tizone* to The Cid and said, "I ask you, Rodrigo, to defend me and my kingdom with the same energy and loyalty you showed to my brother Sancho."

"That I swear to do," The Cid replied.

So Alfonso was crowned King of Castille and established himself with his followers in the royal palace at Burgos. But Alvar Hañez's words had been wise. King Alfonso could never forgive the public humiliations he had suffered at the hands of The Cid and bore in his heart a deep resentment against the champion.

From the moment King Alfonso assumed the crown, the fortunes of The Cid began to decline. His old enemies, the family Beni-Gomez, were now advanced to positions of trust and honor, while his relatives, such as Alvar Hañez, were dismissed from the court. Rodrigo was no longer Commander-in-Chief of the royal armies; he became simply another knight and in the service of a king who distrusted him. The only joy that Rodrigo knew during this time was his marriage to doña Jimena.

The gentle Jimena had long ago forgiven The Cid for the death of her father. They would long since have been married had it not been for Rodrigo's constant battles and wars. Now that The Cid found himself free from these duties he hastened to wed Jimena.

The wedding was celebrated before all the royal court at Burgos with much splendor. And for the next few years, The Cid and doña Jimena knew great happiness together. It was during these years that Jimena bore Rodrigo a son, whom they named Diego in memory of The Cid's father, and two daughters, Maria and Christina. And if The Cid sometimes yearned for the old days of battle and glory, he tried to hide his disappointments. He busied himself with improving his lands at Vivar.

But one fall day, while Rodrigo was out in the fields seeing to the harvest of figs, a royal messenger rode up to him. Alfonso, it seemed, was at long last going to make use of Rodrigo. He required him to go as ambassador to the powerful Moorish Emirate of Granada.

Doña Jimena was sitting in the garden watching little Diego play with his sisters when Rodrigo told her of this. She grew very thoughtful. "What need has the king for an ambassador to Granada?" she asked. "I do not trust him."

Rodrigo frowned. "I had been expecting something like this. You know that the Moorish King of Seville, Motamid, pays

tribute to Alfonso. But lately the Emir Abdallah of Granada
has been threatening to seize this tribute and the city of Seville
itself. I imagine Alfonso wants me to put a stop to Abdallah's
pretensions. It is his duty to protect Motamid as his vassal."

But Rodrigo did not understand the clever workings of Alfonso's mind. It was true that the king was duty-bound to protect Motamid, his vassal. And to make some show of this he was
sending The Cid to restrain Abdallah of Granada. But at the
same time he wished to see the Moors war upon each other.
For this reason, and without informing Rodrigo, King Alfonso
had secretly sent a Castillian squadron to aid Abdallah in his
war against Seville. At the head of this squadron he placed
García Ordóñez, one of his favorites.

When The Cid arrived in Granada he was surprised by
Abdallah's insolent and insulting conduct. But he was even
more surprised to find a Castillian squadron present in Abdallah's army. The Emir of Granada merely laughed at The Cid's
peaceful proposals. He immediately declared war on Seville
and with his army of Moors and Castillians he ravaged the
lands of Motamid.

Enraged by the conduct of Adballah, and even more by the
presence of the Castillian squadron, The Cid gathered together
his small escort and the army of King Motamid of Seville. At
the castle of Cabra he gave battle to the hosts of Abdallah. Long
and hard the two armies fought. But by evening the army of
Granada was broken and fled along with the remnants of the
Castillian squadron. Among the prisoners made by The Cid
was García Ordóñez. After three days, when The Cid was certain that Abdallah would not again attack Seville, he released
his prisoners, sending the Castillians back to Burgos.

When Rodrigo and his men entered the city of Seville in
triumph, their reception was great and joyful. *"Mio Cid, Mio
Cid, Mio Cid!"* the Moors shouted in gratitude. King Motamid
was so grateful for the aid Rodrigo had given him that he not

only paid the tribute due to King Alfonso immediately, but also sent many rich and beautiful gifts to the Castillian king.

Happy at having fulfilled his embassy, the Cid now returned to Castille. He was greeted warmly by the people, but when he arrived at Burgos he found King Alfonso enraged by his conduct. It was only then that Rodrigo understood the double policy the king had been following. But his understanding came too late. Urged on by the family Beni-Gomez and by the humiliated García Ordóñez, King Alfonso, without giving any reason other than the royal pleasure, banished The Cid from all his kingdoms and dominions. He gave Rodrigo nine days to leave the country.

Rodrigo had long ago sworn to King Fernando to defend all of his sons. For this reason he submitted to this unjust sentence without resistance. He hurried home to Vivar to take leave of his wife, Jimena, and his three children. "This banishment cannot be for long," Rodrigo said, trying to comfort Jimena. And although she felt her heart was breaking, Jimena hid her grief. "You will win new honors and King Alfonso will be forced to recall you," she said.

Now in those days, when a powerful noble such as The Cid was banished from a country, all of his vassals were supposed to follow him. They were supposed to help him until the day the king pardoned him and permitted them all to return. Alfonso had given The Cid nine days. During this time the king's sheriffs dismantled all of the houses of The Cid and his followers, leaving the doors open and taking everything of value. Such was always the fate of the banished. Because of this, Rodrigo had to send Jimena and his children to a nearby monastery where they would be under the care and protection of the friendly monks during his absence.

The news of The Cid's banishment traveled quickly through all parts of Castille. When the final day came Rodrigo found himself at the head of three hundred of the bravest knights in all of Spain. They preferred to share his banishment, so confident were they of the glory they would win following his banners.

Before leaving Vivar, The Cid spoke to his followers. "You see how the king treats me and how he will treat all who follow me. He who would change his mind and not ride with me into banishment is free to go."

Before anyone could answer, Rodrigo's cousin, Alvar Háñez, stepped forward. "My Lord, all of us will follow you and you will always have us at your side."

Rodrigo was deeply moved by these words and their proud acceptance by all these knights. Among those who were to follow him he saw Pedro Bermudez, young and eager; Gíl Diaz, proud and defiant, and many many more of his childhood friends. He bent his knees and prayed. "Holy Mary and all the saints, pray for me. May God give me strength to defeat the infidels and help to convert my enemies once again into friends."

Then The Cid mounted upon *Babieca*. With *Tizone* gleaming by his side and his banners fluttering proudly in the breeze behind him, Rodrigo led his small but courageous band of knights on a journey toward unknown perils.

How The Cid Battled Amongst the Moorish Kingdoms

In order to leave the kingdom of Castille, The Cid and his three hundred knights had to pass through the city of Burgos. When they arrived they found every door and window of the city shut tight. They could not know that within the silent houses the people were exclaiming, "How good a knight. If only he served a good king!" And when The Cid would have purchased food and water for his men he found that Alfonso had issued a royal decree forbidding anyone in his kingdom to so much as talk to The Cid. Whoever disobeyed was to have all his property confiscated and to lose his eyes.

So The Cid and his men, silent and saddened, passed through the city and camped for the night by the banks of the Arlanzón river. There they pitched their tents where they could at least water their horses. As Rodrigo was sitting alone in his tent, wondering how he would ever find food and drink for his men, an unexpected visitor appeared. It was Martín Antolínez, a knight and merchant of Burgos. He immediately offered to sell

The Cid everything he needed from his well-stocked ware-
houses.

"Champion," Martín Antolínez said, "tomorrow I will follow
you. In order to help you I must fall under the king's anger.
And to avoid his punishment I prefer to go into exile with you.
Sooner or later the king himself will reward me for what I do
now against his decree."

"Your friendship, Martín," The Cid replied, "is the only good
thing that has happened to me in these hours. I promise you
that everything you now risk will be repaid many times over.
But at the moment I have no money at all, because the king
has taken everything."

"And what will you do?" asked the knight of Burgos.

"The first thing I need is someone to lend me money to maintain my men."

"And who would risk that?"

The Cid glanced up with a smile. "I have an idea. There are
two Moorish merchants in Burgos named Pervez and Moti.
In the past I always sold them the spoils I won in battle.
While we are filling two trunks full of sand, you go secretly
to Burgos and tell Pervez and Moti that I need them urgently.
God knows I hate to cheat them now, but with God's aid I
will soon repay them." Then he gave Martín Antolínez further
instructions and hurried off to find two large trunks.

When Martín found the store of Pervez and Moti, he waited
until he was alone with the two merchants. Then, very mysteri-
ously, he said, "The Cid has gone into exile, carrying with him
two huge trunks full of gold. Since they are too heavy to carry,
and because he is afraid the king will seize them, he is willing
to leave them in your hands if you will lend him some money
which he needs urgently."

Pervez pulled thoughtfully on his white beard and glanced
at Moti who was sitting next to him smoking a water pipe.

"What further have you to say, Christian?" Moti demanded.

"For this service," Martín continued in a whisper, "The Cid will bring you back great riches. But you must promise not to open the trunks nor to break the seals upon them."

Pervez said slowly, "We always thought The Cid carried treasure with him, even though the king forbade it."

"Well then?" Martín asked.

Moti nodded to Pervez. "We will take these trunks," he said, "and we will hide them where no one will ever find them."

"But," Pervez said, "for doing this, and risking the king's anger, The Cid must tell us beforehand what payment he will make."

"Come with me to our camp and speak to The Cid yourselves," Martín said impatiently. "He only wants six hundred pounds in gold from you. You can tell him yourselves what interest you will charge and what reward you want for guarding the trunks."

The two Moors followed Martín from the city with great caution. When they at last reached the tent of The Cid they found two huge trunks waiting for them. The trunks were bound in brass with golden nails and silver handles. Their lids were sealed with scarlet wax impressions of The Cid's coat of arms. The very sight made Pervez's mouth water and Moti's eyes glitter.

The two Moorish merchants quickly handed over the six hundred pounds in gold, mounted the heavy trunks on the backs of mules, and returned in the greatest secrecy with their treasure to Burgos.

As soon as the eastern sky showed the pale blue of dawn on the horizon, The Cid called his men together. "Tell me, *caballeros*," he cried, "where would you have me lead you?"

"Lead us anywhere away from this country where we are not wanted!" said Gil Díaz.

"We will follow you anywhere, Cid," called out Pedro Bermudez.

On hearing these words, Rodrigo ordered the tents struck and then mounted upon *Babieca*. It was a moment of great decision for him. In those days it was generally the fate of an exile to find refuge among the kingdoms of the Moors. But if he did this, Rodrigo knew that he might one day find himself fighting against King Alfonso, a thing he had sworn never to do. On the other hand there were very few Christian kingdoms in Spain against which he had not fought on behalf of King Sancho. So The Cid decided to lead his men to Barcelona. There he would offer his services to Count Berenguer, ruler of the city.

But when they arrived in Barcelona, The Cid found a cold welcome. He was rudely received by Count Berenguer who rejected his services out of hand, and The Cid's men were insulted by the count's followers. The Cid could not know that King Alfonso had sent ambassadors to Count Berenguer to tell infamous lies about him. And Count Berenguer did not foresee that in rudely refusing The Cid's hand, offered in friendship, he might one day have to face that same hand in battle.

Now while The Cid was pondering over what to do in Barcelona, he received one day a letter from Mutamin, Emir of Zaragoza. This Moorish king had never forgotten how The Cid had defended his bride years before and how he had sent her on her way unmolested. Mutamin invited The Cid to bring his men to Zaragoza where they would be sure of a friendly welcome.

Since all the doors of Christian Spain were shut against him, Rodrigo decided to accept this invitation. And when he and his followers arrived in Zaragoza they were received with every honor and with great rejoicing by the people. The Cid was made Commander-in-Chief of the army of Zaragoza, though he warned Mutamin that he would never fight against King Alfonso.

Now Mutamin had a brother named Alhajib, King of Lérida. It was Alhajib's idea to overthrow his brother and thus gain the kingdom of Zaragoza for himself. But when he saw that The Cid was now defending the city, Alhajib realized he would need help. So he wrote to Count Berenguer of Barcelona and to Sancho Ramirez, King of Aragon, asking their help in a campaign against Zaragoza and against The Cid. King Sancho Ramirez of Aragon, remembering how Rodrigo had defeated his champion years before, was only too happy to agree. And Count Berenguer, still believing the lies told by King Alfonso about The Cid, accepted Alhajib's invitation also.

"I swear on my honor," King Sancho Ramirez exclaimed, "that this Cid will never pass the frontiers of Lérida. If he tries, I will give him a lesson he has long deserved."

When these words reached The Cid's ears they only served to make him hasten his preparations. Desiring to strike the first blow, he united the Moorish army of Zaragoza with his three hundred knights and, accompanied by King Mutamin, marched upon Lérida.

With very little interference, despite King Ramirez' boast, The Cid crossed the borders of Lérida and quickly seized the castle of Almenar which stood not ten miles from the city of Lérida itself. But once inside the castle, Rodrigo and Mutamin found themselves suddenly besieged by a tremendous army of Moors, supported by the army of Aragon and Count Berenguer of Barcelona. The situation seemed truly desperate and The Cid held council with Mutamin.

"What is Your Majesty's opinion?" The Cid asked. The two

men were seated alone on a parapet of the castle from where they could see thousands of enemy campfires flickering below them.

"I say let us attack immediately!" Mutamin replied. He was a proud young king with little experience of war.

"I think it might be wiser if you offered to pay your brother something for this castle," Rodrigo declared. "His army is very large, and this way we would avoid unnecessary bloodshed."

Mutamin finally decided to follow Rodrigo's prudent advice. He sent a herald to the enemy camp offering to buy the castle from King Alhajib. But this friendly gesture was understood as a sign of weakness by Alhajib, Sancho Ramirez and Berenguer. They turned down the offer in an insulting manner.

When The Cid heard this news he commanded the trumpets to sound, calling all his men to arms. As always when he was about to go into battle, he was mounted on *Babieca* and wore armor of gold and silver which had been given to him long ago by King Fernando. He balanced a lance with his right hand across *Babieca's* crupper and carried *Tizone* unsheathed in his left. On his shoulder he carried a shield emblazoned with a scarlet dragon. When his small army had gathered behind him, The Cid ordered the great gate of the castle to be opened and led them out.

The Cid and Mutamin charged directly into the ranks of the Moorish soldiers of King Alhajib. So furiously did they fall upon these troops that they soon drove them back into the ranks of the armies of Aragon and Barcelona. It was The Cid's plan that by driving this horde of Moors into their ranks he would cause the Christian armies of King Ramirez and Count Berenguer, unable to distinguish between the Moors of Alhajib and the Moors of Mutamin, to fall upon their own allies. The plan succeeded perfectly. Caught between foe and friend, Alhajib's army was cut to pieces. But The Cid continued to

lead charge after charge, now directly into the ranks of the armies of Aragon and Barcelona. He seemed to be everywhere at once on the field, his sword dealing terrible strokes right and left, while his example inspired his men to great feats of valor. The enemy armies, having helped to destroy their own allies, were now seized by panic and confusion. It seemed there was no end to these Moors and the terrible corps of Christian knights that fell on them again and again like thunderbolts. It was not very long before their lines wavered and then broke. The defeat quickly became a rout and then a disaster. King Ramirez and King Alhajib fled the field. But Count Berenguer and many of his men were cut off and fell prisoner to The Cid.

Two days after this notable victory, Rodrigo asked Mutamin to release the Christian captives. The Emir generously consented and Count Berenguer and his men left Almenar not only with their freedom but also with their arms and horses. It is possible that the count now regretted having insulted Rodrigo. But if he did, his pride would not let him admit it.

On his return to Zaragoza, The Cid was acclaimed by the people as if he and not Mutamin were the real king of the city. The humble folk knew that it was The Cid and his three hundred knights who were their best protection. Mutamin showered honors on The Cid and from that day forth made him his Chief Counselor. But all of this did nothing to make Rodrigo forget his dream of returning to Castille. He sent half of all the spoils he had won from Alhajib to King Alfonso. But it seemed that nothing could soften that monarch's heart.

Now there was within the kingdom of Zaragoza a city called Rueda. The mayor of this city, a Moor named Abulfalac, had recently been caught stealing from the city treasury. But before he could be called before King Mutamin, the clever mayor decided on a measure that might save his life. He left the city of

Rueda secretly by night and went to the court of King Alfonso in Castille. He offered to turn over the city of Rueda to Alfonso if only the Castillians would protect him from King Mutamin. King Alfonso, knowing very well that The Cid would never fight against him, eagerly agreed to this proposal.

One dark and stormy night not long afterward, King Alfonso and a small group of knights arrived secretly outside the walls of Rueda. Neither Mutamin nor The Cid knew that the Castillians had even crossed the border, so quietly and quickly had Alfonso moved. When midnight arrived, Abulfalac opened one of the portals to the town and Alfonso's knights entered. But there they fell into the trap that Abulfalac had treacherously devised. This schemer had played a double game. It was true that he feared Mutamin, but the way in which he hoped to escape punishment was not to make Alfonso a gift of the city of Rueda but rather to make Mutamin a gift of King Alfonso. So when the Castillian knights entered the city they were killed, every one, by men who waited in ambush. It was only through the greatest luck that Alfonso himself and a handful of knights remained outside the city walls.

As soon as news of this treacherous action reached Zaragoza, The Cid called together his three hundred knights and rode immediately to Rueda. There he found King Alfonso and his few remaining knights preparing to depart once again for Castille. But it seemed very doubtful that the little group could ever fight their way to the border. Presenting himself before King Alfonso, Rodrigo offered all his help. "Your Majesty must know that neither King Mutamin nor myself had any knowledge of this treachery," he declared. "Mutamin has given me permission to take vengeance now on Abulfalac."

It had been many months since King Alfonso had set eyes on The Cid. When he saw him again standing before him he felt the old stirrings of jealousy. But his situation was desperate. Without Rodrigo's protection he had small hope of ever returning to Burgos.

"We are too few now, Rodrigo, to take this accursed city," Alfonso said. "Let Mutamin execute vengeance on that traitorous dog. But since you here prove yourself such a faithful and loyal vassal, you may return with me to Castille, Rodrigo."

When he heard these words, The Cid's heart leaped within him. It seemed as if his dearest dream would now come true. Although Alfonso had said nothing of lifting his decree of banishment, Rodrigo felt that this was only a formality. He accepted the king's offer in the name of himself and all his men, with great joy.

The next day, King Alfonso with his handful of knights, guarded by The Cid and his three hundred, took the road to Castille. It was a hard thing for The Cid to give up his splendid position in Zaragoza and to part from his friend, King Mutamin. But the promise of returning to his own country swept all such thoughts from his mind.

A few days later Rodrigo de Vivar was reunited with his wife, Jimena, and his three children. The good monks had guarded them well. The Cid's happiness was very great. He passed his days within the monastery with his family and waited for King Alfonso to lift the decree of banishment. It seemed as if a new life would now open before him.

But King Alfonso could never abide the joyful reception Rodrigo had received everywhere in Castille. His jealousy returned and he treated Rodrigo with great coldness, showing his displeasure at every opportunity. And of course the tongues of The Cid's old enemies, the family Beni-Gomez, never ceased pouring lies into Alfonso's ear.

It was not long before Rodrigo understood that he was only tolerated in Castille and that Alfonso had no intention of lifting the decree of banishment or of returning his lands and properties to him. He feared, indeed, that he would soon be sent away again. To forestall this he appeared before the king one day and said "Sire, I see that my presence is not agreeable to you. I beg your permission to depart."

"Go with God, Rodrigo," Alfonso replied drily.

So with his heart heavy and his high hopes shattered, The Cid once again took leave of his family and returned to the kingdom of Zaragoza. It was not long before his faithful knights rejoined him there.

Now when The Cid had left Zaragoza to accompany Alfonso back to Castille, King Alhajib of Lérida and King Ramirez of Aragon once again saw an opportunity to seize Mutamin's kingdom. They raised another large army and advanced toward the borders. It is easy to imagine the relief and joy felt by the people of Zaragoza when they found that The Cid and his knights had returned to protect them.

When Rodrigo learned of this new war he decided to attack at once. "Alhajib and King Ramirez think themselves on the offensive," he explained to Mutamin. "They will not expect a flanking attack into the very heart of Lérida."

Gathering his knights and the army of Mutamin, Rodrigo led them over the borders of Lérida to the field of Olocau del Rey, near the great fortress of Morella. His strategy proved sound. As soon as they learned of this unexpected invasion, Alhajib and King Ramirez turned from their own offensive and hastened to the defense of Morella. For if that fortress fell, the way to Lérida would be open.

It was night and The Cid was making his way from campfire to campfire admonishing his men to be brave, when a messenger arrived from Alhajib and King Ramirez.

"Sir," the messenger proclaimed, "my king, Sancho Ramirez of Aragon, commands you to abandon all these lands that are properly owned by his friend Alhajib, King of Lérida. If you do not do this immediately, he will be obliged to teach you a sharp lesson."

"Tell your lord," Rodrigo replied quietly, "that I shall not move my encampment from where it is. If the King of Aragon wishes to pass through this territory in peace I will serve him with good heart and even give him one hundred of my best knights for escort."

As they watched King Ramirez's emissary ride off, Alvar Háñez muttered to Rodrigo, "Your words will certainly enrage Ramirez and Alhajib. Their army is much larger than ours. Perhaps it would be best after all to retreat and offer battle on some better occasion."

"I swear not to move from this spot nor to strike my tents," Rodrigo replied.

Alvar's words proved true. King Ramirez and Alhajib grew very angry when they heard The Cid's answer. The following morning they led their army to the attack.

The battle lasted all day. But The Cid had calculated well. With the enemy fortress of Morella in their rear and the enemy army in front, his army could only hope to survive through victory. They fought like wounded tigers, charging again and again with desperate fury into the ranks of the enemy. Alhajib and Ramirez's troops were tired from their ceaseless marching. But it was The Cid himself who was decisive. His mighty arm struck blow after blow with *Tizone* and by evening the army of King Ramirez and Alhajib was in full flight from the field. When his men would have pursued the enemy, Rodrigo held them back. "Always leave a path of retreat open to a defeated army," he said. "It is because we had no way of retreat that we fought so well."

The Cid and King Mutamin captured two thousand prisoners that day and a very rich booty. Once again Rodrigo released all

of the captives except sixteen of the leading nobles. These he kept as hostages against any future attack by King Alhajib.

While Alhajib and King Ramirez, gathering together the small remains of their once powerful army, retreated to the city of Lérida, Rodrigo and his men returned in triumph to Zaragoza. There they were received with great enthusiasm, and still more honors were heaped upon them by the grateful Mutamin.

Following the custom of those days, Rodrigo was entitled to keep one-fifth of all the spoils for himself. But after the victory at Morella, The Cid called together one hundred of his best knights. He loaded them with his fifth of the spoils and placed Alvar Háñez at their head.

81

"Go to Castille, Alvar," Rodrigo said, "and present these gifts to the king. Try to persuade him to lift his decree of banishment."

"I have no doubt of success," Alvar said, "seeing how justly you treat him."

"And go also to my wife and tell her that with God's help I hope we shall soon be reunited."

And accompanied by the hundred knights, Alvar Háñez rode to Castille. There he presented himself before Alfonso and begged the king to pardon Rodrigo. But although he accepted The Cid's gift, King Alfonso would not lift the decree of banishment.

Alvar Háñez and his knights returned sadly to Zaragoza. "Rodrigo," he said, "Alfonso declares it is still too soon."

Rodrigo sighed. He was seated alone at the council table in the royal hall of King Mutamin's palace. "I see. And what did he say of my present?"

"The king said that since you won it from Moors, he would accept it." Alvar Háñez paused. "But there is more important news."

"What is it?" Rodrigo asked, trying to hide his disappointment.

"While I was at the court in Burgos I heard rumors of a plan by which Alfonso hopes to conquer all of the Moorish kingdoms in this region. I would not be surprised if he attacked Zaragoza very soon."

This last news troubled The Cid mightily. He got up and strode up and down the great hall, his head bowed in thought, his footsteps ringing hollowly against the cold stone. At last he said, "If King Alfonso of Castille attacks Zaragoza, we must abandon the city."

"And where will we go?" asked Alvar Háñez.

"Somewhere. Anywhere. Some place where I will not have to fight against my own king."

Not long afterward the suspicions of Alvar Háñez were fulfilled. The army of King Alfonso of Castille, supported by the army of King Ramirez of Aragon, laid siege to the city of Zaragoza.

The Cid, as soon as he saw the Castillians surrounding the city, went immediately to King Mutamin. He felt as if he were being split in half but he bore himself with dignity. "Mutamin," he said sadly, "you know I swore long ago never to fight against the children of good King Fernando."

Mutamin put his hand on Rodrigo's shoulder. "I know that, *Mio Cid*. I prefer that you remain true to your oath. You are free to go in friendship."

And so, with a heavy heart, The Cid led his three hundred knights from the city of Zaragoza that same afternoon. They rode to the city of Tudela and there awaited the outcome of the war.

It was not long before Alfonso's plans began to bear fruit. First the Moorish kingdom of Toledo and then Valencia were forced to acknowledge him as overlord. Meanwhile the siege of Zaragoza was drawn tighter and tighter. In desperation Mutamin offered to pay Alfonso a large sum of gold in tribute. But the Castillian king sent back this message: "The gold that you offer and the city—everything you possess—is already mine!" And the siege continued.

King Mutamin, in his despair, called upon Rodrigo to defend the city. But The Cid turned a deaf ear to his pleas. Finally Mutamin went so far as to offer to surrender his city of Zaragoza to The Cid, proclaiming him king, rather than surrender it to Alfonso. But Rodrigo remained loyal to his oath and refused every offer.

His victories had by now made Alfonso overconfident. He pressed the Moorish kingdoms cruelly and would not negotiate with them unless they surrendered completely to him. He was now called "Emperor of the Two Religions" by his courtiers, and his pride overruled his wisdom.

In their distress, the Moorish kings of Seville, of Granada and of Badajoz met together in the city of Granada. They all realized that it would not be long before they were conquered by Alfonso unless they received aid. But help was not far away. Just across the Straits of Gibraltar, in Africa, lay the Moorish Empire of Morocco, ruled by a fierce and warlike tribe called the Almoravides.

Seated in the beautiful gardens of the Alhambra, smoking water pipes, the three kings considered what to do.

"We must call upon Emperor Yusuf and his Almoravides for help," the king of Seville exclaimed.

"Not so quickly," the king of Granada replied. He was an old man with a long white beard. "Emperor Yusuf is an ambitious man and his Almoravides are the fiercest warriors in all of Islam. If we call upon him for aid, he may remain to conquer us as well as the Christians."

"But King Alfonso will surely conquer us in any event!" the king of Badajoz exclaimed.

"Better even to be conquered by Yusuf than by a dog of a Christian!" the king of Seville declared. "Besides, we have no reason to think that Yusuf will not respect our thrones."

"I see that you are determined," the old king of Granada sighed. "So be it. I have two excellent couriers at my disposal. They shall go at once to Morocco!"

And so Alfonso's cruel policy, dictated by pride, forced the Moors of Spain to seek aid from their brothers in Africa. The Cid, by messengers from Tudela, had begged Alfonso not to press the Moorish kings too severely. But the monarch had turned a deaf ear to all advice.

Neither Alfonso, nor The Cid, nor even the Moors of Spain, could have imagined the terrible whirlwind of disaster that was about to descend upon them.

How The Cid
Conquered the Levante

The Almoravides were a tribe of desert Moslems who had conquered everyone in their path all across North Africa. They burst upon Islam at a time when the older Mohammedan kingdoms had grown fat and peaceful and forgetful sometimes of the teachings of the Koran. Led by a *fakir* named Abdallah ben Yassin, these religious fanatics preached a return to the earlier purity of Mohammedanism. Against any who opposed them they proclaimed the *jihad*, or Holy War.

None could be found to stand against this Holy War of the Almoravides. Their numbers were great and their spirits fierce. Each soldier believed with all his heart that if he were killed in battle he would go straight to Paradise as Mohammed had promised. They were expert horsemen and rode swift Arabian chargers. They could go for weeks eating only wild berries and drinking camel's milk. And finally, in their Emperor Yusuf they had a leader of great military genius and of great ambition.

Yusuf was a small, wiry man with a short black beard and the glittering black eyes of a fanatic. He lived in great simplicity, wearing only the coarsest monk's cloth and eating the commonest of foods. Since he had conquered all of North Africa, his ambition now sought new fields of glory. He had glanced from time to time at the map of Spain. He had long dreamed of bringing the Holy War not only to the Christians but also to the decayed Moorish kings of that wartorn peninsula. But he was too clever a commander to attempt a landing across the Straits of Gibraltar in the face of an entrenched enemy. He bided his time for several years, awaiting an opportunity. From his empire in Morocco he had watched how Alfonso grew bolder and harsher in his dealing with the Moorish kings, confident that sooner or later these kings would have to seek his aid.

He did not wait in vain. When the two messengers sent by the kings of Seville, Granada and Badajoz arrived at Yusuf's court, he received them at once. They prostrated themselves on the floor before Yusuf's throne and handed up their message. Yusuf read it carefully and then bade the messengers rise. "You may tell your kings," he said softly, "that the Holy War of the Almoravides will arrive in Spain."

One of the messengers bowed his head and spoke. "Oh, Great Emperor, our royal masters bid us also ask you to swear to respect the Moorish kingdoms of Spain and direct your *jihad* only against the accursed infidels."

Yusuf smiled enigmatically. "You may tell your kings that the Holy War of the Almoravides will arrive in Spain," he repeated. Then he dismissed the messengers.

Within a few weeks Yusuf had collected a mighty army and hundreds of ships to carry it across the Straits to Spain. But as the soldiers and horsemen were going aboard the ships, the emperor fell to his knees and cried out, "If this be a mistake,

87

Allah, send us heavy seas and a storm that will prevent our sailing! But if this be for the good of Islam, send us a quiet sea and favorable winds!"

The wind was steady to the north and the sea remained calm. Within a few days Yusuf had landed an army of one hundred thousand men at Algeciras to bring the terrible scourge of the *jihad* to Spain.

The news of the landing of this huge army spread quickly to all parts of Spain. Everywhere men trembled, for the fame of these fierce warriors and their reputation for cruelty had gone before them. When King Alfonso of Castille heard of the landing he knew he would have to raise the siege of Zaragoza. So he sent one last message to King Mutamin within the city offering to give up the war if Mutamin would pay him a certain sum of money. But it was too late. Mutamin also knew of the arrival of Yusuf. He sent a cold answer back to Alfonso bidding him look to his own kingdoms which must now fall before the power of Islam. Seeing that his promises and threats were now to no avail, Alfonso quickly led his army back to Castille. From Burgos he sent messengers to all parts of Christendom seeking help against the Almoravides.

"My Lord," said Alvar Háñez, who happened to be visiting the royal court, "send for The Cid and he will come running to our aid!"

"For what?" Alfonso demanded ironically. "Sitting there in Tudela he has probably forgotten how to fight by now!" he added, laughing.

The Kings of Aragon and France and Italy sent armies to help Alfonso, and many brave knights and nobles from every part of Europe joined him at Burgos.

On the other hand, all the petty Moorish kingdoms of Spain now united under the leadership of the Emperor Yusuf. Those who had paid tribute to Alfonso in the past now denounced him. The Moors saw in Yusuf a chance to put an end to Christian pretensions in Spain and to reduce every infidel to slavery.

But as his army swelled in size, King Alfonso once again allowed his pride to overcome his judgment. Instead of awaiting Yusuf's attack in strongly fortified positions, he went in search of the Almoravide army. He found it encamped three miles from Badajoz on the plains of Sagrajas. Seeing that the Moslems did not offer to attack him he gained even more confidence. Early in the morning he led his army to the attack.

Alfonso did not realize that he was entering a trap. The front ranks of the Moslem army were composed of troops from the Moorish kingdoms. These, as Yusuf had expected, broke and fled before the terrible onslaught of the heavily armored Christian knights. They ran for the walls of Badajoz, closely followed by Alfonso's army.

But the farther the Christian knights pursued the Moors, the deeper into the trap they fell. For the Almoravides themselves had not yet come into battle. They waited on the edge of the plain. Yusuf, watching from a nearby hill, waited until the Christian charge had almost reached his own tents. Then he signaled with his scimitar and sent a large division of Almoravides to attack the Christian army at the rear. Confused by this unexpected interference, Alfonso's men turned to fight the new enemy. But when confusion was greatest in the Christian ranks, Yusuf ordered his entire Almoravide army upon them. Suddenly thousands upon thousands of fierce Moslem warriors charged into the disorganized ranks of Christians. Their terrible battle cry was almost drowned by the awesome sound of the rolling of their drums—which were now heard for the first time in Spain.

The Christian knights found themselves surrounded. They did not know which way to turn to fight. There was no time to organize a defense, no time to even organize an escape.

Men fell in thousands and the nearby streams turned crimson with blood. The clashing of steel upon steel, the neighing of terrified horses, the cries of the wounded and the steady rolling of the Almoravide drums made the battlefield sound like the workshop of the God of War.

Then, when the battle was at its height, with death and defeat stalking the Christian ranks, Yusuf unleashed to the attack his personal bodyguard of four thousand African horsemen. It was the final blow. Alfonso's army fell to pieces and the Castillian king himself was badly wounded by a lance thrust. Only the coming of night prevented the killing or capture of every one of the Christians by Yusuf's victorious troops. Alfonso, accompanied by a handful of badly wounded knights, barely escaped with his life by hiding behind a nearby hill and then making his way to the castle of Coria by night.

Many thousands of prisoners and a huge booty fell into the hands of the Almoravides. It was their most important victory and the greatest defeat ever suffered by Christian arms in Spain. After the battle, the fanatical Emperor Yusuf commanded that all the prisoners be beheaded. This was done, and the heads of the Christians were loaded into carts which were then sent to all the Moorish kingdoms of Spain, as a sign of the great victory won by Islam and of the end of the Christian power in Spain.

It was a hard lesson that Alfonso learned on the plains of Sagrajas—and it was all due to his pride and to the poor advice of his counselors. Now once again he called for aid from all the kings of Christendom. But this time he did not fail to call also upon The Cid. By royal messenger he promised Rodrigo full pardon if he would come to the defense of Castille. He arranged to meet The Cid at the city of Toledo.

A few weeks later Rodrigo and his men presented themselves before the royal encampment at Toledo. As soon as they ap-

peared, King Alfonso himself advanced to meet them. But The Cid quickly dismounted and, followed by his fifteen best knights, knelt before the king, bowing his head humbly.

"Arise, *Mio Cid*," the king said.

"Sire, I wish to receive my pardon at your feet," The Cid replied.

"Know then, Rodrigo de Vivar and all men present, that I hereby revoke my decree of banishment. From this day forth I give you my friendship and will receive you in every part of my lands," Alfonso proclaimed.

"I thank God in heaven and I thank Your Majesty," The Cid said, kissing his sovereign's hands in the age-old sign of submission.

Most of those who witnessed this act of reconciliation were overjoyed by it. But, as always, there were a few jealous men, including the family Beni-Gomez, who looked with envy on the scene.

When the royal court returned to Burgos, the king quickly restored to Rodrigo and all his followers their homes, castles, lands and possessions. All the people of Castille celebrated The Cid's return with holidays and rejoicing. And Alfonso's knights began to regain a little of the faith they had lost at Sagrajas.

But in spite of having won the king's friendship, Rodrigo found himself under the strictest orders not to participate in any battles or raids into the Moorish lands. Henceforth he was to serve Alfonso at court, one among many nobles who advised the king.

More than one year passed in this manner. The Cid observed a discipline that ill suited him. His impatience was soothed only by the happiness he now found with his wife, Jimena, and his three children. But many a night Rodrigo dreamed of the old days, when, mounted on *Babieca*, he had rushed against his enemies, causing them to flee by his mere presence.

The truth was that the Moors, after their great victory, were content to remain in peace and offered no threat to Alfonso for the moment. Seeing themselves freed from paying tribute to Castille, the Moorish kings showed no signs of pressing home their great victory. Yusuf had led most of the Almoravide army back to Africa. There he planned to reorganize for a final conquest of the entire peninsula. With his departure the Moorish kingdoms of Spain soon fell to squabbling amongst themselves again.

But King Alfonso had his own plans. He soon put them into operation, this time counting on the support of The Cid. Time and cruel defeat had changed the king's attitude. He was now willing to play a more cautious game against the Moslems.

With the exception of Seville and Badajoz, which were large and extensive kingdoms, most of the Moorish states in Spain were small territories surrounding some large city. To conquer them each separately, taking advantage of their jealousies and quarrels, was Alfonso's plan. When one day he received a call for help from Alcadir, King of Valencia, who was being attacked by Alhajib, King of Lérida, Alfonso immediately sent The Cid at the head of a large army to relieve Valencia. Before the fatal battle of Sagrajas, Valencia had paid tribute to Alfonso. It was the king's hope that The Cid, after driving off the king of Lérida, would once again force Valencia to pay tribute.

But when Alhajib learned that his old enemy, the dreaded Cid, was once again on the march, he lifted the siege of Valencia and fled back to Lérida without a battle. When Alcadir saw that he was free from danger, and that his enemies had fled simply at the mention of The Cid's name, he once again acknowledged Castille's overlordship to Valencia and paid Alfonso the tribute due for his protection. Besides that he heaped honors and rich gifts on Rodrigo. All of these, along with the tribute, were sent at once to Alfonso.

Finding himself without a battle to fight, Rodrigo now made

93

a long and careful study of all the lands, kingdoms and cities near Valencia. They were all ruled by Moors and the entire area was known as the Levante. He saw that these regions were poorly defended and would easily fall before a careful and energetic campaign. He returned at once to Burgos to lay his ideas before King Alfonso.

"Sire, give me permission to conquer these lands," he begged.

"I do not believe it is possible," Alfonso answered. "And besides, you know I can give you no aid for the moment."

"I need no more than your permission, Sire."

"And you have no fear of the Almoravides?"

"It is against them that my plan is directed. Whoever controls the Levante controls the gateway to the north and to the south. As for Yusuf—I will find ways to defend myself against him."

"In that case, leave as soon as possible and fight for Castille," the king said. "And I assure you, Rodrigo, whatever lands and honors you win from the Moors shall be yours and your descendants' forever."

Confident of Alfonso's support, The Cid quickly gathered together a large body of knights. Among them were many who had followed him before, such as Alvar Háñez, Pedro Bermudez, Gil Díaz and Martín Antolínez. They quickly left Castille to conquer or die among the Moors.

Although Alfonso had acted generously with The Cid, it was partly because he already had news that the Almoravides would soon return, and all of Rodrigo's dreams would surely be shattered. Alfonso could never abide that The Cid should be as important and beloved as himself in Spain.

Rodrigo had barely crossed the borders of Castille when he learned that his old enemy, Count Berenguer of Barcelona, was laying siege to Valencia. Since Valencia was already under the protection of Alfonso and was the capital and center of the very lands The Cid hoped to conquer, he immediately led his army to the relief of the city. But wishing to avoid an unnecessary battle, Rodrigo sent a letter to Count Berenguer demanding that he withdraw. The count, after much thought about the size of Rodrigo's army, reluctantly but peacefully returned to Barcelona. Alcadir, King of Valencia, seeing his city once again saved by The Cid, welcomed Rodrigo and his men with honors and rich gifts.

Using Valencia as a base, The Cid made his way through all the lands of the Levante. Everywhere he went he was joyfully received by the common folk who trusted him despite his being a Christian. They were tired of the countless quarrels and raids of their masters and longed for peace. The petty kings of the Levante, seeing the strength of Rodrigo's army and knowing his fame, quickly submitted to the sovereignty of Castille and paid tribute to King Alfonso. Thus, without fighting a single battle, simply through prudence and his own reputation, The Cid was able to organize the entire Levante for Castille.

But in spite of these bloodless victories and the rich tribute that Rodrigo sent daily to the court at Burgos, his enemies around King Alfonso never ceased to whisper their accusations. The worst among them was the family Beni-Gomez, who had never forgiven The Cid for the terrible defeat he had inflicted on them many years before at Carrión. Instead of closing his ears to this gossip, Alfonso, still jealous of The Cid's reputation, weakly listened.

"Rodrigo has said that he alone is enough and more than enough to defeat all the Moors," whispered the Beni-Gomez.

"The boaster said that?" Alfonso demanded furiously.

"And he said that if he had been in command at Sagrajas the battle would have turned out differently."

"The fool!" roared King Alfonso. "I have it in mind to banish him once again!"

In this manner the family Beni-Gomez and their followers

95

chipped away steadily at the faith and friendship Rodrigo had earned from Alfonso.

It was during these times that the famous Castillian knight García Jiménez held the castle of Aledo in the very middle of the Moorish lands. This knight made constant raids and incursions among the Moors with his twelve thousand warriors. This thorn thrust into the middle of their kingdoms greatly troubled the Moorish kings. For this reason, and also because of The Cid's rapidly spreading domains in the Levante, the Moorish kings once again called on Yusuf and the Almoravides for help. Yusuf, deep in his planning for the coming invasion of Spain, sent a part of his army that quickly surrounded the castle of Aledo and laid siege to García Jiménez and his brave twelve thousand.

King Alfonso heard of the arrival of this Almoravide army and was informed by spies that their force was not very great this time, so he immediately gathered together an army for the relief of Aledo. He sent dispatches to The Cid ordering him to bring his own army to meet Alfonso at the town of Villena. From there they would march with combined forces against the Almoravides.

Rodrigo lost no time in gathering together his men and marching to Villena. He posted advance scouts everywhere to inform him as soon as they caught sight of Alfonso's troops.

But Emperor Yusuf had learned that a mighty host was about to descend upon his army at Aledo. He therefore asked the Moorish kings of Spain to supply him with men, since it was now too late to send reinforcements from Africa. But the Moorish kings lived in superstitious awe of The Cid and they refused to do battle against him. Yusuf decided that the Moors of Spain needed one more lesson. He lifted the siege of Aledo and left the Moors to their fate.

King Alfonso, whose spies were everywhere, learned of this

while still on the road to Villena. Without informing The Cid, he changed his plans and marched directly to Aledo. After seeing that García Jiménez was now safe, he returned to Burgos.

The Cid waited for several days at Villena. Then he also marched to Aledo. But by the time he arrived King Alfonso had departed.

Here was meat indeed for the wicked tongues of the Beni-Gomez. Back in Burgos they spoke of nothing else.

"The Cid disobeyed your orders, Sire!" said some.

"By not arriving at Aledo with his army he placed your life in great danger," others whispered.

"He is a traitor. He abandoned you and exposed you to death at the hands of Yusuf!" others maintained.

These accusations and many others finally caused King Alfonso to take action against The Cid. He began by stripping him of the lands and castles he had given him. Then he seized all Rodrigo's riches and possessions. Finally he even arrested doña Jimena and her three children.

When The Cid learned the fate of his family, he came within a hair's breadth of rebelling and overthrowing Alfonso. But, after much inner struggle, he contented himself with sending Pedro Bermudez and Gil Díaz to ask Alfonso his reasons for such unjust actions.

So great was the king's rage that he refused to receive these knights. Instead, he banished them from his kingdom. But, in spite of his anger, Alfonso knew there were certain limits he dare not overstep with The Cid. Therefore he released doña Jimena and her children from prison.

"Go to your husband," King Alfonso shouted, "and tell him I never want to see him again in any of my kingdoms!"

"Sire, you do a grave injustice to Rodrigo," Jimena answered bravely.

"I want no traitors in my court!" Alfonso cried.

97

"Your Majesty is surrounded by traitors!" doña Jimena said. "There is no one in all of Castille as loyal to you as The Cid!"

But the king, furious at these words, simply turned away, thus ending the interview.

Now The Cid found himself alone and friendless. Of course he was overjoyed when doña Jimena and the children joined him outside Valencia. And his faithful band of knights never deserted him. But the Kings of Aragon and Navarre had never forgiven the defeats he had inflicted upon them. Count Berenguer of Barcelona was his sworn enemy. The Moorish Emirs of Zaragoza, Lérida, Seville, Badajoz and Granada, seeing that The Cid no longer enjoyed the support of Alfonso, quickly turned cold toward him. And there was always the threat that Yusuf and the Almoravides would one day return.

Calling his bravest and most faithful knights into his tent, Rodrigo told them, "Every hand is now raised against us. There is no place to go. We shall have to maintain ourselves here at Valencia by naked strength. We may have to fight alone against all of Spain—although I will never fight against Castille. What say you?"

Alvar Háñez stepped forward. "We told you once, Cid, that we would follow you through victory or defeat and that we would always be at your side. We will never desert you!"

Hearing these words, Rodrigo raised his head and smiled. "So be it then! Here we shall stand alone against all the world if necessary."

It was not long before Rodrigo's words proved true. Alhajib, King of Lérida, seeing that The Cid was abandoned by King Alfonso, made haste to enter into an alliance with Count Berenguer of Barcelona. These two thought that their chance to destroy their old enemy had come.

But when The Cid learned of what was planned against him, he did not wait to be attacked. Instead he marched his men, fighting on the way, to the plains of Teruel deep within the borders of the Kingdom of Lérida. Teruel was an excellent place for a small army to withstand the assault of a much larger force. And The Cid had guessed correctly, that his invasion of Lérida and seizure of Teruel would sting Alhajib's pride so badly that the Moorish King would attack at once, without awaiting a more favorable opportunity.

Rodrigo and his men spent the days and nights before the coming battle erecting log barriers, digging pits, building small stone embrasures and placing pointed stakes at an angle into the ground. Their plan was to force the large enemy army to fight on a narrow front, where their numbers would not help them.

Nevertheless, when Alhajib and Berenguer arrived at Teruel, their armies were so large that more than one of Rodrigo's men gave himself up for lost. But like the veterans they were, they patiently waited behind their barricades for the assault, determined to sell their lives as dearly as possible.

Count Berenguer now tried to provoke The Cid into leaving his fortified positions. He sent him the following letter:

"Tomorrow, at breakfast, with God's mercy, you will see me approach very close to your lines. If you leave your fortifications then and attack us, you will truly be Rodrigo de Vivar, he who is called the Champion. But if not, you will be a base coward. And all the bravery of which you boast will not help you. Know that we shall never leave here without you, either dead or in chains!"

Rodrigo did not bother to answer this insulting message. Instead he used it as part of a stratagem. He pretended to be very frightened by it and allowed Berenguer to think that he would try to escape. He ordered all his tents struck and preparations made as if for flight.

Berenguer, thinking his enemy was about to slip away, divided his army into many small groups and sent them to occupy all the roads and paths that led from Teruel. During the following night it was an easy matter for Rodrigo and his men to surprise and capture each of these small groups, making them prisoner one by one.

The following morning, Count Berenguer thought The Cid was now surrounded, so he attacked with his diminished army. But instead of a fleeing enemy he was suddenly confronted with a horde of knights who fought like desperate lions. His men fell back from the shock and tried to defend themselves, but without hope. Their horses fell into the pits that had been prepared for them, or butted up against the sharp stakes that had been planted. Berenguer's knights found themselves surrounded by log barriers and stone embrasures from which showers of arrows poured into them. And all the while, The Cid and his knights charged them again and again until at last they were broken and fled from the field.

Count Berenguer himself and five thousand of his men fell prisoner to The Cid. And now, for the second time, Rodrigo showed his generosity. He realized that both he and Count Berenguer were victims of King Alfonso's lies. There was no cause for a quarrel between them. But Berenguer was a proud man. It would not be easy to convert him into a friend.

While resting in his tent after the battle, Rodrigo was visited by the captured count. Berenguer was strongly bound and closely guarded by several knights. His armor was shattered and he bore more than one wound, but he held his head high.

"Cid," he said, "I beg you the mercy of forgiving my past offenses and granting freedom to myself and my men." This was the standard plea always made by the defeated after a battle. Neither Berenguer nor Rodrigo was accustomed to seeing it granted.

The Cid did not answer. He simply glanced at his defeated enemy and, with a wave of his hand, said, "Guard him well."

But once the count had been led away, Rodrigo called several of his knights and ordered them to see carefully to Berenguer's wounds and to treat him with the greatest respect. He also ordered the finest foods for his unwilling guest. The rudeness with which he had treated him in his tent was only meant to humble the pride of the Count of Barcelona. Rodrigo realized this must be his first step in any campaign to win Berenguer's friendship.

But shortly afterward a soldier presented himself before Rodrigo's tent. "Cid," he said, "Count Berenguer refuses to eat."

The Cid immediately followed the soldier to the place where Berenguer was held. He saw that his captive was sad but still defiant. "What is the matter, Count?" he asked. "Do you not wish to eat?"

"I would not touch one morsel for all the food there may be in Spain," the count replied. "I prefer death to the shame of this defeat."

"Eat, Count, and drink my wine," Rodrigo said firmly. "If you eat you shall be a free man. But if you refuse to eat you will never again see your own lands however long you live!"

"Eat your own food, Rodrigo! May it please you! My only happiness now will be death."

"Count," Rodrigo replied patiently, "if you will eat to my satisfaction, I will not only free you, but also all of your knights."

Count Berenguer looked up unbelievingly. "If you would do that, Rodrigo," he said slowly, "I would never forget your generosity as long as I live."

"Then eat, Count. You have my word. When you are finished, you and all your men are free."

And the count, along with his five thousand men, ate a huge banquet prepared for them by Rodrigo. The Cid had acted very wisely. By making the freedom of his followers depend upon

the count's eating, he had given Berenguer an excuse—even an obligation—to accept his generosity. And once having eaten The Cid's food, Count Berenguer could never, on his honor, be an enemy.

While he ate, Count Berenguer thought upon all this himself. For when he had finished he smiled at Rodrigo and said, "Cid, keep your promise now and set us free. I understand what you have done. And I swear to you that since I became a count I have never eaten so well. I will never forget the pleasure of this meal."

Rodrigo offered his hand and Berenguer took it. "Go with God, Count," he said, "and may we be friends from now on." Then Rodrigo gave orders that the count's sword be returned to him and horses supplied for Berenguer and his men.

"Thank you, Cid!" Berenguer said before he departed. "I shall never forget this!" Then, spurring his horse, the count led his men across the plains of Teruel.

This tremendous victory, against very great odds, greatly increased The Cid's fame. His very name had become a word of superstitious terror among his enemies. Alhajib, once more defeated, returned to his city, where he suddenly died.

It was while he was returning from the victory at Teruel, pondering on the sudden death of Alhajib and receiving messages of congratulations from all parts of the land, that Rodrigo fell ill.

He was taken to the monastery at Daroca and there he hovered between life and death for several days with a very high fever. When he recovered he found that his first visitor was Count Berenguer of Barcelona.

"I heard of your illness and came at once," the count said, standing by Rodrigo's bedside.

"I am very grateful—"

"I want you, also," Berenguer interrupted, "to honor me with your friendship and alliance."

"It is I who would be honored by—"

"No, no," Berenguer interrupted again, "you deserve the greatest honor for your courage and knightliness. Everyone admires you."

Rodrigo smiled sadly. "Not everyone, Count. If you but knew—"

"But I do know!" Count Berenguer interrupted for the third time. He had the impatient air of a man who brings important news. Grinning broadly, he finally could contain himself no longer. "Rodrigo, you know that Alhajib is dead. And you know that he paid tribute to me and was my vassal. His kingdom of Lérida is mine to dispose of. I hereby give it to you and to your descendants forever!"

Rodrigo could hardly find words to thank the count. From a

lonely outcast surrounded by enemies, he had suddenly become overlord of Lérida, with the entire Levante at his feet and with the powerful support and friendship of the Count of Barcelona —a man who only yesterday had been his sworn enemy.

The Cid now found himself master of all the lands of the Levante. Among all those Moorish kingdoms, none could be found to fight against him. Those who had been cold of late now hastened to pay him tribute and seek his protection.

It was thus, more through his generosity and knightliness rather than through his victories, that Rodrigo de Vivar became Lord of Lérida and a permanent power in the lands of the Moors.

How The Cid Became King of Valencia

The Cid had won his overlordship of Lérida at a time of great danger. He could count on the aid of Berenguer of Barcelona and Alcadir, King of Valencia. But Alfonso of Castille never ceased scheming about how to conquer what were now The Cid's lands. And more menacing still, the dreaded Almoravides had returned to Spain—this time determined to conquer all of it.

All those Moorish kings who had first called on the Emperor Yusuf for help regretted their decision. Yusuf's mighty army moved from city to city, from kingdom to kingdom, crushing the Moors of Spain. As if the conquered had been Christians, the victors took their territory, sent their kings into exile in Africa and established the Almoravide power throughout the south of Spain. To the eyes of Yusuf and his fanatics, the easygoing and jealous Moors were traitors to the purity of the Koran, and he brought against them the dreaded *jihad*, the very Holy War he reserved for infidels and Christians.

Rodrigo understood clearly that his most deadly enemy was Yusuf. For this reason he took steps to unite the small territories around him to resist the Almoravides. Since the Moors were now more fearful of Yusuf than of The Cid, this was not a difficult task. More than that, he started to fortify the mountains which separated the lands of the Levante from the Almoravide hordes. Within a short time, by constant vigilance and the heaviest labor, The Cid established a fortress area that was a sharp thorn in the flank of the Almoravide army and a constant threat to their further advance.

The onrush of Yusuf's army seemed to be irresistible. The African emperor soon conquered all of southern Spain and then turned his eyes toward Valencia and Lérida. It was intolerable to him that this insolent Rodrigo de Vivar should maintain a Christian army on his flank. Besides, Yusuf's plan for crushing Alfonso of Castille and the remaining Christian kingdoms of Spain could not be put into effect until The Cid was crushed. But Yusuf had a clever scheme for capturing Valencia with very little bloodshed.

Within the city of Valencia itself there were very many who, through fear or greed or religious fanaticism, would welcome the arrival of the Almoravides. These discontented and traitorous people were led by one Ben Jahhaf, also called *El Zambo*. Ben Jahhaf was in secret correspondence with Yusuf and together these two hatched a plan.

Yusuf started sending raiding parties into the lands near Valencia. Wherever they went they burned and killed, leaving nothing but ruins and corpses behind them. Although Rodrigo knew it was dangerous to leave Valencia unguarded, he could not stand idly by while his neighbors cried for help. So he led his men forth from the city and, within a few weeks, had trapped and completely destroyed the Almoravide raiders. The campaign was short but brutal, and one evening as Rodrigo was standing wearily outside his tent watching his men prepare for the return march to Valencia, a messenger rode up. His horse was flecked with foam and the man himself had a bloody wound on his arm. His breath was short and he gasped out his words as if they might be his last, "O Cid, you must return to Valencia at once! King Alcadir is dead and *El Zambo* has seized the city! He rules now in the name of Emperor Yusuf and the Almoravides."

While The Cid's army made haste to depart, Rodrigo had the wounded messenger taken into his own tent. There his wounds were bandaged and he was given food and water. The story he told was a tragic one.

Yusuf's raiding parties had been only a trick to get The Cid out of Valencia. Once Rodrigo's army had left, *El Zambo* and his followers rose in rebellion. With the help of secret Almoravide agents within the city they won over some of the army and captured the royal palace. King Alcadir and all his family were beheaded and his treasures seized by *El Zambo*. Then, when he found himself fully in control of the city, *El Zambo* had executed all of Alcadir's friends and followers and every Christian he found within the walls, including some of The Cid's sick and wounded men. To make this treacherous victory even more secure, an Almoravide army, led by the son of Emperor Yusuf, had appeared before the walls of the city. Now that army had withdrawn, leaving a small garrison, and *El Zambo* ruled Valencia in the name of Yusuf.

As Rodrigo listened he felt anger and sadness fighting for mastery within him. His friend King Alcadir, the king's family, and all those helpless warriors who had counted on his protection—all dead. The silence within Rodrigo's tent grew heavy. At last he raised his head. "Bring me paper and pen!" he ordered in a voice that shook with rage. And this is the letter he wrote to Ben Jahhaf, *El Zambo*:

"I, Rodrigo Diaz de Vivar, name you and all of your followers as traitors. I swear by God and by Saint Mary, that I shall avenge the death of King Alcadir, and I shall pursue you always and everywhere until you have paid the price of your crimes."

The Cid's army marched that very night. But as he reviewed his knights and infantry filing slowly down the road to Valencia, Rodrigo worried. He knew that as soon as Yusuf heard of his return, he would send another Almoravide army to crush him. Caught between *El Zambo* within Valencia and the Almoravides without, his situation would be extremely dangerous. It was impossible for him to storm the city itself. He would be forced to fight an army many times the size of his own on the open plains before Valencia. What he needed was a fortress near the city and some means of limiting the field of action.

When his army neared Valencia, The Cid suddenly ordered his men to take a new road and march directly on the fortress of Villanueva which stands not far to the north of the city. From here he could cut off most supplies to Valencia and at the same time protect himself against the advancing Almoravides. He now had his fortress and, unknown to his men, he also had a means of limiting the field over which they would have to fight.

Just as Rodrigo had expected, the Emperor Yusuf had already sent a tremendous Almoravide army from Africa which marched rapidly to Valencia. When they learned that The Cid had established himself in the fortress of Villanueva, Yusuf's commanders hurried there with this fanatical horde.

Some of Rodrigo's men now trembled to find themselves trapped, as they imagined. "If we do not abandon Villanueva at once we shall be surrounded!" they exclaimed. "Why have we locked ourselves up in this fortress to be starved out by the armies of Yusuf?" others demanded. Some of them pointed out that unless they fled at once they would have to fight their way

out. And on the open fields that would be impossible against Yusuf's vast army.

But Rodrigo went among them and calmed their fears. So great was their faith in him that his very presence seemed to put cowardice to flight. "I promise you," he said, "that Yusuf's army will not long besiege us here. And the fields will not be open. We shall be able to fight our way out on a narrow front."

The very next day the terrible drums of the Almoravides could be heard rumbling in the distance. By afternoon they had appeared in their thousands to the north of Villanueva. The Cid and certain of his knights watched from the battlements of the fortress. "If we would act, Cid, this is our last chance," said Alvar Háñez. "By evening we will be completely surrounded." The Cid smiled at his old friend. "Then we must wait for evening," was his only reply.

Alvar Háñez's prediction proved true. The misty light of the setting sun showed the Almoravide hordes camped in every direction around Villanueva. And their lines were close to the fortress.

When Rodrigo had carefully inspected the enemy camps from the battlements, he turned to his lieutenants. "Now is the hour to strike!" he said.

Alvar Háñez gasped. "You would attack them in the open field now, when all hope of escape is gone?"

The Cid smiled. "Why did you think, Alvar, that I seized this fortress of Villanueva?"

"Why—because it is strong, it guards Valencia from the north—"

"Yes, yes," The Cid interrupted. "But have you forgotten that the great locks that control the irrigation canals of all the plains hereabout are located in the dungeons beneath us? Follow me!"

Alvar Háñez, Pedro Bermudez, Gil Díaz, Martín Antolínez and several others hurried after Rodrigo down into the cold stone dungeons of the castle. There they found the huge wheels that raised the sluice gates of the irrigation canals. On The Cid's orders they began to turn them.

Now all the lands around Villanueva were irrigated by these canals. By adjusting the sluice gate wheels within the fortress, water could be directed into any field for miles around. The Cid's men opened all the gates at once and the effect was catastrophic.

In the fading twilight the Almoravides did not notice the irrigation canals around them filling up. Slowly but surely the water rose until at last it overflowed the canals and spilled out onto the fields on which Yusuf's army were encamped. Suddenly the Almoravides found themselves encamped in a swamp where movement was almost impossible. And the darkness of the night added further to their confusion. And still the waters rose. The Moslems began to panic. They did not understand what had happened or how the steady land beneath them had suddenly become a quagmire. To them it seemed a miracle and their superstition increased their terror. Everywhere about them in the darkness they saw horses slipping and disappearing. Within an hour the mighty army became a horde of panic-stricken men, each trying desperately to save his own life. It was in vain that Yusuf's commanders went among them trying to bring some sort of order into that night of horror. The Almoravide army fled, killing thousands of their comrades in their haste. The first faint light of dawn disclosed an empty water-filled plain all around Villanueva on which floated the remains of tents, harnesses, banners and weapons. Silence reigned over those fields.

For three days The Cid and his men waited within the fortress for the water to subside and to see if Yusuf's army would return. But finally one of The Cid's scouts reported: "The Almoravides have fled all the way to Granada. They say you are a wizard, Cid, and destroyed their army through magic."

111

Rodrigo smiled. "We have defeated them with the help of God," he replied. "Now let us enter Valencia!"

But the inhabitants of Valencia, seeing the Almoravide army disappear as if by magic, had risen up against the cruel Ben Jahhaf and the small Almoravide garrison. They quickly chased the troops from the city and placed *El Zambo* in prison. Then they sent messengers to The Cid who was approaching the city with his army fresh from the victory at Villanueva.

When Rodrigo saw the messengers approaching, he halted his columns and dismounted from *Babieca*. Alvar Háñez, Pedro Bermudez, Gil Díaz and others of his closest friends stood beside him. Sunlight glistened from the distant towers and minarets of Valencia, making it seem like a golden crown set down in the rich green valleys.

The messengers reined up their horses when they were within a few yards of The Cid and his men. They dismounted and knelt before him. "O Cid," they declared, "the people of Valencia have risen against the false Ben Jahhaf and his Almoravide guards. The traitor is in prison and the Almoravides have taken flight. We are without an army now and without a king. Rodrigo de Vivar, we offer the kingdom into your hands to defend and to hold for all times and unto your farthest descendants."

"Is this the will of the people?" Rodrigo asked.

"It is, Sire," the messengers replied.

Rodrigo frowned thoughtfully. None of his friends spoke now. In the silence that surrounded them they could hear the distant crowing of cocks saluting the dawn. Finally The Cid spoke. "Messengers! Return to your city with this message: I, Rodrigo de Vivar, have never had a kingdom. But I have defended your city against every enemy, and I have prayed to God to protect and make it prosper. If I serve the people of Valencia with justice and mercy, may God permit me to hold this kingdom. But if I do wrong, may He strike the crown from my head!"

The messengers hurried back to the city with Rodrigo's message and not long afterward, The Cid and his army marched into Valencia through the great northern gates. The entire population came out to cheer them and to throw flowers in their path. The principal men also, judges, counselors and the holy men of Islam, greeted The Cid with great courtesy. They conducted him to the royal council chamber within the palace. There The Cid ordered Alvar Háñez to distribute the army throughout the fortifications and to prepare the city for defense against the return of the Almoravides. When that was seen to,

Rodrigo ordered the traitor, Ben Jahhaf, brought before him. He had not forgotten his oath to avenge King Alcadir.

El Zambo was dragged into the council chamber in chains. The once proud and insolent ruler of Valencia trembled now as he read the meaning on the faces of the city counselors. "I am innocent!" he whined. "I was forced to do what I did by the Emperor Yusuf."

The Cid raised his hand for silence. "Do you swear to be innocent of the death of King Alcadir and to possess none of his treasure?" he demanded.

"I swear! I swear!" Ben Jahhaf cried.

"Are any to be found to accuse this man?" Rodrigo asked.

One of the oldest and wisest of the city counselors now stepped forward. He stroked his long white beard and stared with hard eyes at the chained criminal. "Now, by Allah," he exclaimed, "you have added perjury to your crimes, Ben Jahhaf. I accuse you of murdering King Alcadir and all his family, including his innocent children, without mercy. I accuse you of having sold our city to the power of the Almoravides. I accuse you of having murdered the principal advisors of King Alcadir and their families without pity. And I accuse you of having stolen King Alcadir's treasure."

"Lies! Lies!" Ben Jahhaf screamed. "These men hate me, Cid! They lie!"

"Ben Jahhaf," The Cid said, "if you have sworn truly I promise to set you free and to protect you. But if you have sworn falsely you will be judged with the same mercy you showed to King Alcadir. Who offers proof?"

The old counselor clapped his hands twice and two guards immediately appeared. Between them they carried a large metal chest which they set at Rodrigo's feet. "Here, Cid, is the treasure of King Alcadir which was found in Ben Jahhaf's house. See for yourself!"

"That is a lie!" Ben Jahhaf screamed. "They put that chest there themselves to be found! I never saw it before!"

The old counselor motioned to the guards and they opened the chest. Within were piles of rubies and emeralds and diamonds and every kind of precious stone. And sitting on the very top of this sparkling treasure was a single golden crown with an intricate design, set with two huge star sapphires.

Ben Jahhaf, shaking with fright, now shouted hysterically, "Now, now you see the proof, Cid. These men prepared this chest. There was no such crown among King Alcadir's treas—" Ben Jahhaf fell suddenly silent. He had just convicted himself with his own lips.

"No, traitor, there was not!" the stern old counselor declared.

"But only someone who had examined the treasure carefully could ever know that!"

In quick succession now witnesses were brought forth who could swear to the truth of all the charges against *El Zambo*. At last Rodrigo turned to the traitor and said, "Ben Jahhaf, what defense do you make against all these accusations?"

El Zambo, seeing that all hopes were now gone, drew himself up and sneered. "Very well then, Cid. What they say is true! What I have done I have done for the good of Islam! The day is coming when you will feel the power of Emperor Yusuf. Take care how you treat his good friend!"

The Cid pondered for a moment and then spoke. "Ben Jahhaf, you are guilty of cruel murder, of robbery, and of perjury. You say you have done these things for the good of Islam. So be it. I leave your fate to these wise men of Islam. As for Emperor Yusuf, I do not fear him." Turning to the city counselors he asked, "What is your judgment?"

"Guilty!" they said with one voice. "By our laws, Cid," the eldest of them declared, "this man should be stoned to death by the populace."

"Then justice must be done," The Cid said.

And *El Zambo* was carried off to his richly deserved fate.

In the days that followed, Rodrigo showed himself to be a merciful and just ruler. He respected the laws, customs, and religion of his subjects. He introduced several new laws to help the poor and to encourage trade and learning. He always listened respectfully to the advice of his Moorish counselors and soon won their admiration for his generosity and fairness. But in one matter he would not agree with them. They wanted to crown him King of Valencia at once. But Rodrigo declared that it would be presumptuous of him to accept a crown he had not yet fully earned. For he knew that he would have to fight the Almoravides again.

When the Emperor Yusuf saw the remnants of his army return to Africa and heard of the defeat, his rage was great.

"The Cid is my enemy forever!" he shouted. "I swear by the Koran to revenge myself upon him!"

"This Cid is a wizard, Your Majesty," one of his advisors whispered in a trembling voice. "At Villanueva he drowned our army by magic!"

"Wizard or no," Yusuf declared, "I live now for vengeance. I will exterminate this dog of a Christian!" He glared at his advisors. "And those impure Moslems of Valencia who have welcomed him into their city—they shall die! Yusuf has never been defeated!"

And the Almoravide emperor gathered together a huge and mighty army which he sent against The Cid. By his orders it disembarked on a beach not far from Valencia and immediately raised the black banners that meant "no quarter."

When The Cid learned of the arrival of this tremendous army he at once ordered the great gates of Valencia closed. Then he posted his men on the walls, ready to repel any attack. He had already provided the city with food and water. Very soon the huge army of Almoravides appeared, blackening the plains for miles around, so great was their number. But Rodrigo went from post to post along the battlements of the city, reassuring his men and encouraging them by his own calm courage. "They are many," he said, "but we have stout walls around us and brave hearts within."

All that night the Christians watched from the walls of Valencia as thousands and thousands of campfires sparkled in the fields around the city. And with the dawn came the first attack.

The Almoravide army, commanded by Yusuf's nephew, Mohammed, rushed with fury against the walls, carrying scaling ladders and grapples. So high were the towers and so fiercely did Rodrigo's men defend them that these attacks were soon repelled. But as soon as one division of these fanatic warriors was driven back, another rushed forward to take its place. Like the waves of a stormy sea, the Almoravides beat against the walls of Valencia.

Every day the attacks continued, and every day they were repulsed. It seemed as if Mohammed was determined to break into Valencia even if he had to climb over the dead bodies of his entire army to do it. But in reality he knew that with so many men, he could afford much greater losses than the Christians could. And hunger must soon stalk the city.

After a few days of these frenzied assaults, The Cid's commanders grew uneasy. "They will overwhelm us with sheer weight of numbers," Pedro Bermudez observed. "We lose very few men each time they attack," Martín Antolínez pointed out, "but our numbers are so small that we shall soon be defeated."

"We must defend ourselves to the end and trust in divine mercy," The Cid replied. "These Almoravides are only men, fanatic though they may be."

The Cid's words proved true. For ten days Mohammed's army hurled itself against the mighty walls of Valencia. With each attack thousands of them died. And although Mohammed was determined to conquer at any cost, his men were not. After the tenth day it was seen that their assaults grew weaker and more cautious. Spies brought word that among the rank and file of the Almoravides there were mutterings against this slaughter and many who said The Cid was a wizard and it was hopeless to fight against him.

Now seeing that Mohammed's army was growing demoralized by their heavy losses and by superstition, Rodrigo devised a plan to trap them.

One dark night The Cid secretly left the city followed by several hundred of his bravest and strongest knights. They followed ravines which hid them from the eyes of Almoravide sentries. They reached a small woods on the flank of the sleeping enemy army, and waited there until dawn.

At the first light of day, Rodrigo led half of his knights in a furious charge against the still sleeping enemy camp. The Almoravides had never expected an attack. Panic quickly spread among them as they tried desperately to arm themselves and mount their horses.

As soon as The Cid saw that the Almoravides, although still in great disorder, had gathered together to repel him, he ordered his men to retreat as if in terror. They raced back to the woods with Mohammed's cavalry hard after them.

But at that moment the other half of Rodrigo's knights burst from the woods and fell on the flank of the Almoravide cavalry like avenging angels. Immediately Rodrigo and his men turned once again to the charge.

The Almoravides now found themselves beset on two sides by furious hordes of Christian knights. First confusion and then panic began to spread among them. And it was at that moment that the great gates of Valencia opened to disgorge the entire Christian army onto the plain.

What now took place was not so much a battle as a massacre. With their cavalry trapped by The Cid and his knights, the enemy infantry was exposed to the merciless charge of thousands of horsemen. The Almoravides, now certain that The Cid was a wizard and his men demons, already confused and terrified by the attacks which poured into them from every side, threw down their weapons and fled. Thousands were killed and thousands were captured. Their entire army was broken and driven back to the sea. There a few of them, including Mohammed, their commander, made their escape in the boats which had brought them.

So great was the booty found in the Almoravide camp that every one of The Cid's men became rich. But Rodrigo carefully reserved one-fifth of all this treasure and sent it to King Alfonso of Castille.

That monarch, so easily swayed, had been watching all The Cid's battles and campaigns. It had finally been driven home to him that Rodrigo was indeed loyal, and that the whispers of his courtiers were nothing more than slander. Alfonso was greatly pleased by The Cid's victory. When Rodrigo's gifts were placed before him by Gil Díaz, in a burst of generosity he declared, "Now we see clearly who is the real leader of Spanish Christendom!" He sent his best wishes to Rodrigo, and from that day forth he never again listened to the lies of the family Beni-Gomez.

Now that he had won this second great victory over the Almoravides and saw that his lands were secure for some time at least, Rodrigo permitted himself to be crowned King of Valencia by the grateful Moors of the city. But no sooner had he received this honor than he immediately sent Alvar Háñez to King Alfonso to place the newly won kingdom at Alfonso's disposal. This was the duty he felt he owed his overlord, the King of Castille. When Alfonso heard Alvar Háñez's message he rose from his throne, gripping his jeweled sword of state. "We hereby accept the Kingdom of Valencia in vassalage to Castille," he declared. "But know all men that Rodrigo de Vivar is rightful king of that city and all the lands pertaining to it. We accept this honor in symbol only. In Valencia let Rodrigo rule, our honored friend and ally from this time forth!"

And so Rodrigo found himself a king and once again the trusted champion of Alfonso of Castille. But more than that, since he was the only commander in all of Christendom who had never been defeated by the Almoravides, and since his kingdom of Valencia barred the way north to Yusuf's armies, he found himself also the accepted leader of all of Christian Spain.

Now The Cid hastened to make alliances with all who opposed Yusuf. His old friend Count Berenguer of Barcelona was the first to acknowledge his leadership. And since King Sancho of Aragon had recently died, Rodrigo lost no time in making a treaty with Pedro, Sancho's son, the new king of Aragon. The Kings of Navarre and Zaragoza, and the Emirs of Toledo and Seville also hurried to come under The Cid's protection.

And it was well that they did. For in Africa, the Emperor Yusuf had by now become obsessed with but one desire——to kill The Cid and to conquer all of Spain. His days and nights were filled with schemes and intrigues to effect his purpose. But Yusuf had become cautious now, and he bided his time until his preparations should be complete.

Rodrigo took advantage of these months to fortify his kingdom and to administer it so wisely that he won the affection of every inhabitant. His days were filled with this labor and his nights with planning for the coming storm. He could not know that fate, which had so often smiled upon him, was now to deal him a cruel and heavy blow from a totally unexpected quarter.

How The Cid Suffered Cruel Misfortune

In this chronicle of treachery and heroism, of battles and wars, perhaps we have neglected to speak fully enough of The Cid's family life. Except for the time of his banishment from Castille, doña Jimena was always at Rodrigo's side, as were his son, Diego, and his daughters, Maria and Christina. Whenever Rodrigo left Valencia on an expedition against the Almoravides, it was doña Jimena who took his place at the head of the council of state. Her wisdom and courage had more than once saved The Cid from impatience or error. Maria and Christina had grown up to great beauty. They inherited their mother's grace and something of Rodrigo's great pride. Since so much of their lives was spent among the Moors, both Rodrigo's daughters and his son benefited from the fine education which in those days could be had only in Moslem countries.

The Cid took greatest pride in his son, Diego. From the time the lad could hold a wooden sword Rodrigo had taught him everything he knew about fighting, horsemanship, archery, hawking and all the knightly accomplishments. But in knight-liness Diego needed little instruction. It seemed as if he had inherited his father's boldness and generosity, his gentleness and courage. Diego was the idol of The Cid's army, second only to his father.

Ever since Diego reached the age of fourteen, Rodrigo had allowed the lad to accompany him on minor expeditions in order to train him for his inheritance. For by the law of nations and the promise of King Alfonso, Diego would one day rule the kingdom of Valencia. Later, when Diego entered early manhood, he fought often by Rodrigo's side, showing a valor and courage which promised much for the future. The Cid was immensely proud of his son, but in battle he never permitted him to fight alone. He was fearful that Diego, carried away by youthful ardor, might commit some fatal mistake. Like fathers before and since, The Cid felt that his son was only safe at his side.

One day a messenger arrived in Valencia sent by Alfonso, King of Castille. He brought grave news. The Almoravides, striking suddenly from the south, had invaded the lands around Toledo. Alfonso was calling upon all his vassals to support him with their armies in a campaign against the invaders.

As soon as Rodrigo heard this news he called a council of state. His first impulse was to lead an army to Alfonso's support. But his wise counselors pointed out that this might well be a trap set by Emperor Yusuf. With The Cid absent from Valencia, the Almoravides would find it easier to conquer the city.

For this reason, and also because Diego had reached the age at which it would be well for him to assume the responsibilities of command, The Cid decided to send his son with a large part of his army to Alfonso's aid. He sent the following letter to the King of Castille:

"Sire, I send you my son in place of myself, with the hope that he will do honor to his name and to Castille."

In command of a numerous and well-equipped army, Diego left Valencia to join Alfonso in Castille.

The Almoravides, once again commanded by Yusuf's son Mohammed, laid waste the lands around Toledo with their usual ferocity, killing and burning without mercy. King Alfonso did not delay striking at them. He quickly gathered his army and offered battle to the Almoravides on the fields of Consuegra.

But in spite of the fierceness and courage of the Christian knights and their heroism in the face of greater numbers, Alfonso suffered a bitter defeat. Many of his soldiers were killed or captured, and among the dead was Diego, The Cid's only son. The Castillian king and a handful of survivors made good their escape from this disaster, and from Burgos, Alfonso sent The Cid the cruelest news he had ever received.

When Rodrigo learned of the death of his son, his sorrow was so great that he suffered a collapse. He was put to bed and there hovered between life and death for several weeks. It was at this time that doña Jimena showed the nobility of her spirit. Although she too had been crushed by this misfortune, she tried to hide her sorrow sufficiently to encourage Rodrigo to live. It was partly through her efforts that The Cid recovered finally from the shock. But it seemed also, to many of his friends and followers, that Rodrigo Diaz de Vivar was being saved for a greater purpose—that of humbling the pride and crushing the ambitions of the Almoravides.

When The Cid had recovered sufficiently to resume his duties as ruler of Valencia, all his thoughts were bent on revenge. Doña Jimena tried to dissuade him. "Remember," she said, "you are a Christian." But nothing could shake The Cid's determination to wipe out the Almoravides wherever and whenever he found them. He now made daily raids beyond the borders of

Valencia, carrying death and destruction to every Almoravide castle and stronghold in his path. But still he was not satisfied. These were minor victories in his eyes. Perhaps fortunately for The Cid, he could not offer battle at this time to the main armies of Yusuf. For the great defeat at Consuegra had placed all of Christian Spain temporarily on the defensive.

King Alfonso of Castille now once again sent out messengers to every Christian nation of Europe, begging for help against the Moslems. Slowly but surely his armies were rebuilt and began to regain the confidence they had lost at Consuegra. Alfonso had also gathered wisdom over the years. He knew now without question that only under The Cid's leadership could his armies hope for victory over Yusuf. But his court was still full of Rodrigo's enemies, especially the family Beni-Gomez, who had never forgiven The Cid for their defeat years before on the plains of Carrión. To overcome their hostility and to re-unite all of Christian Spain, Alfonso now determined on a masterful piece of strategy. He arranged a betrothal between the two sons of the Beni-Gomez family, the Counts of Carrión, and the daughters of The Cid.

Rodrigo and doña Jimena were well pleased with this match, since the Counts of Carrión were well-born and highly placed nobles in Castille. They gladly invited the two youths to Valencia and there the betrothal took place. It was arranged that the marriages should be celebrated at the royal court in Burgos, and a firm treaty of peace and friendship would then be established between The Cid and his old enemies the Beni-Gomez.

One day while Diego and Fernando, the Cid's prospective sons-in-law, were discussing matters with some of Rodrigo's advisors in the palace at Valencia, The Cid's pet lion broke loose. This lion had been a gift of the Moorish king of Zaragoza some years before and was always kept in a cage in the great council room. It happened that at the moment the tremendous beast broke free Rodrigo was sleeping on a bench not far away. Great terror swept through the council chamber. Some of The Cid's men stood before their sleeping master with cloaks outspread to protect him from the lion. Fernando was so frightened that he hid under a bench, while his brother Diego ran screaming from the chamber, crying out, "I will never see Carrión again!"

The noise roused Rodrigo from his sleep. Glancing around, he saw his knights cowering before the roaring lion while counselors and advisors ran from the chamber. He yawned, stretched, and walked over to the lion. When the huge animal saw The Cid coming toward him he stopped roaring and bowed his head as if in shame. Rodrigo seized his mane and led him back to his cage. Then he turned and laughed reproachfully at his knights. "And where are my future sons-in-law, Fernando and Diego?" he demanded. When they were at last found, their faces were still white with fear. And although Rodrigo never mentioned the incident again, the Counts of Carrión were bitterly shamed by what had happened.

The day soon arrived when the Counts of Carrión were to escort their betrothed back to Carrión, where they would be entertained until the day of the wedding at Burgos. Doña Jimena and Rodrigo were sorry to see their daughters go, but they supplied them with rich clothing and a great treasure as their dowry. And with them they sent the good and faithful old knight Felez Muñoz as their guardian.

Rodrigo and his knights accompanied the party as far as the borders of Valencia. There The Cid, who had so recently lost his son, took a tearful farewell of Maria and Christina. But Alvar Háñez touched his elbow and said, "It is time now to return to Valencia, Cid. If it please God you will have many an occasion to visit your daughters in Carrión."

The Cid smiled then and nodded. "That is true." Turning to

his daughters he said, "I commend you to God. Behave in such a manner that shall give us reason for pleasure and pride."

Fernando and Diego now rode forward. "May God grant that it be so," they exclaimed. Then they made a courteous farewell and rode away with their attendants, and with doña Maria and doña Christina.

Now unbeknownst to The Cid, or to King Alfonso, or to Maria and Christina, the family Beni-Gomez had entered into this alliance with a false heart. The hatred they bore Rodrigo for their defeat at Carrión still rankled in their breasts. They had agreed to this betrothal with the hope and plan of disgracing The Cid and making him appear a fool before all the world. Besides that, the young counts, Fernando and Diego, were both greedy and cowardly. They hoped to seize the rich dowry that Rodrigo had given his daughters and they also feared that one day Maria and Christina might tell the story of how they had fled from the lion, thereby shaming them eternally. But so clever were they at hiding their true feelings that none guessed what was in their hearts. For it is always hard for honest and true people to believe evil of those around them.

The Counts of Carrión traveled day and night until they came to the range of mountains which borders the kingdom of Castille. There they felt secure from The Cid, and as the country was wild and uninhabited, they thought that no one would ever come to know of what they now planned.

When they had reached the woods known as Corpes, high in the mountains, The Counts of Carrión ordered tents pitched and camp made for the night. Then at the first sign of dawn they ordered their camp struck and all their followers to ride on ahead of them. They said that they would escort Maria and Christina alone for a while to enjoy the beautiful morning air.

As soon as they found themselves alone with the Cid's daughters, Fernando spoke up. "Now we shall tell you," he said, "that in our hearts we still bear the greatest hatred for your father. For you we have nothing but contempt since you were not born of a noble family."

"We will leave you here in these mountains," Diego said, "to die of starvation or perhaps to be torn to bits by wild beasts!"

Maria and Christina could hardly believe their ears. They were so stunned that they could find no words to express their horror. Finally Christina, biting back tears of shame, said, "Since you ran with fright from my father's lion, you should consider how far you will run from my father when he hears of this!"

The mention of the lion, however, only enraged the two counts. Seizing their hard leather bridle reins they started to

whip the Cid's daughters unmercifully. "The Cid will never learn of this, and if he does," they shouted, "it will be his shame forever!"

If they expected Maria and Christina to cry out in fear and pain, the Counts of Carrión were mistaken. Although the reins cut them cruelly, The Cid's daughters refused to plead for mercy. Instead, Maria said, "You have two swords—why do you not kill us now? We are not afraid to die, and one day you will pay for this!"

But the counts, driven to fury by their own fear and by the great courage of The Cid's daughters, simply beat them with greater fury until Maria and Christina collapsed. Leaving them there for dead, Fernando and Diego now rode off to join their followers.

Now when the Counts of Carrión had ordered all of their men to go ahead of them through the mountains, Felez Muñoz, the old knight who had been appointed guardian of his daughters by the Cid, had become suspicious. He rode a while with the others but then turned his horse aside and waited by the road, hidden among the trees, to be certain that the Counts intended no mischief. When he saw them ride by alone, their faces contorted with fierce laughter, his heart leaped with alarm. He dared not show himself for fear they would kill him on the spot, but instead he waited until the sound of their horses' hoofs had faded in the distance and then made his way quickly back to the woods of Corpes. There he found the Cid's daughters, apparently dead.

The good old knight rushed over to them and took them in his arms. When he heard their hearts beating he muttered a prayer of thanks. From a nearby stream he brought water, and dressed their wounds as best he could. Finally they opened their eyes. With tears of shame they tried to tell him of what had happened. But Felez Muñoz had guessed all. "Quickly,

quickly," he whispered, "for the love of God, we must flee from this spot. When the Counts of Carrión miss me from among their followers they will return here and murder us all!"

So saying, the knight placed Maria and Christina upon his own horse, covered them with his own cape and, taking the reins in his hand, led them from the woods of Corpes by secret paths. They traveled thus for two days and a night without pause or rest. Finally they arrived at the borders of Valencia and from there were escorted by the border guards to the city.

When The Cid heard what had happened he became speechless with rage. While doña Jimena tended to her daughters he called his advisors to him and immediately made plans for a war against Carrión to exterminate the family Beni-Gomez finally and completely. But doña Jimena came into the council room. Glancing around, she saw the expressions on the faces of Rodrigo's knights, and his own deathly pallor of rage. "You are planning a war against Carrión?" she asked calmly.

"Not so much a war as an extermination of these vile pigs!" Alvar Háñez said.

"I have sworn by my beard," The Cid declared, "that the Counts of Carrión shall be punished for this by death!"

Doña Jimena frowned. "My Lord and husband," she said quietly, "it was King Alfonso who arranged this betrothal. It is from him that you should demand justice in the normal way. If you make a private war on Carrión you will be simply revenging yourself and you will cause deep dissension throughout all of Castille. We have need now of unity to face the Almoravides. Justice is better than revenge and does more honor to your name. Our daughters are not seriously hurt and we shall yet find them noble husbands."

At these words a look of shame came over Rodrigo's face. He knew that doña Jimena spoke the truth. As he glanced at his advisors and knights he saw that they too had been per-

131

suaded. "Very well," The Cid said at last. "We shall seek justice from King Alfonso. But if he does not grant it, I shall enforce it myself."

The news of the insult suffered by the daughters of The Cid now spread throughout Spain. The Counts of Carrión could not refrain from boasting of how they had humbled the mighty *Campeador*. To them it seemed the only proper way to avenge the defeats their family had suffered at his hands.

When word of what had happened reached King Alfonso, his first reaction was one of outrage. He had arranged this betrothal and he felt as insulted as Rodrigo. But in a calmer moment he realized that his kingdom was now threatened with civil war. For if The Cid exacted his own vengeance Alfonso intended to support him. But it would mean splitting away part of his subjects' loyalty. And with the Almoravides constantly threatening further war, that could be a very grave risk. So when a messenger arrived from Valencia asking for justice in The Cid's name, Alfonso's pleasure was great. He knew now that even to avenge his own daughters, Rodrigo would not bring civil war to Castille. It was the final proof of The Cid's great loyalty.

Alfonso acted immediately. First he dismissed the family Beni-Gomez from his court and stripped them of all their honors. Then he announced that he would hold a Royal Court in Toledo to do justice to The Cid within seven weeks' time.

The Counts of Carrión realized then that they could not hide behind Alfonso. When they begged the king to forgo his Royal Court, they were threatened with banishment from Castille. But if they fled, they knew The Cid would hunt them down to the ends of the earth.

Rodrigo made very careful preparations for the court. He gathered together one hundred of his best knights and made the journey to Toledo. There he pitched his camp outside the city walls and awaited the appointed day.

Early on a bright and sunny afternoon the Royal Court was

convened on a grassy field just outside the walls of Toledo. In the distance could be seen the snow-capped towers of the *Sierras*, while the field itself was covered by richly hung tents, blazing like jewels in the clear sunlight. All the great knights of the land were present as well as bishops, archbishops, dukes, counts, and nobles of every kind. The king's throne had been set up at a far end of the field. He was attended by five hundred knights in full armor, and his banners spread like a rainbow in the air above him. In his right hand he held the great jeweled sword of state. As soon as the trumpets had sounded he spoke. "We, Alfonso, King of Castille, León, and Galicia, and Overlord of Toledo, Seville, Zaragoza, Valencia and other lands and kingdoms too numerous to mention, hereby declare this Royal Court convened. Let there be peace at this court between both parties. Let the learned men of the law look closely and faithfully into all that is spoken here today."

The king nodded to the three judges who sat upon a raised platform nearby hung with silks and ermines, and continued,

"For ourselves, be it known by all men that we have only one side—the side of justice. Let the Cid, Rodrigo Diaz de Vivar, step forward and make his complaint."

Rodrigo arose and walked in great dignity to the center of the field. He bowed to King Alfonso and then to the judges. "Sire, my Lord Justices, and all men, I hereby declare that the Counts of Carrión, who have injured me in a way known to all of you, are thieves. For when they took my daughters to be their betrothed, I gave them many riches and treasures as a dowry for my daughters. Since they have abandoned my daughters, all these riches are truly stolen. They have returned nothing of all this to me."

Alfonso spoke. "What say you, Counts of Carrión, to this charge?"

Now both Fernando and Diego whispered quickly with their advisors. They were surprised that The Cid would choose to bring only a charge of theft against them and they thought that if they settled with him on this account he might be satisfied to let the matter rest there. Finally Diego spoke. "Sire," said he, "all men know that we are of very high birth. We are descended from the ancient line of Carrión. We should be wed to the daughters of kings or emperors, not to the daughters of a petty adventurer. When we abandoned his daughters we did well. We kept the dowry as was our right, in payment for all our troubles. But to keep peace in this land, we agree to repay him."

The Cid's brows gathered together like a thunder cloud when he heard these words, but he kept his peace, saying only, "Then let the thieves return my treasure to me here and now."

"We have spent all of those riches," Diego replied, "but we shall repay him from our lands of Carrión."

The judges whispered together and then the oldest of them spoke, "O Counts of Carrión, you shall repay The Cid here and now. The payment cannot be in lands but must be in kind. That is our judgment."

Count Fernando now spoke up. "But we have brought no such treasure with us!" he exclaimed.

"Go to seek for it!" King Alfonso thundered. "This court shall recess for three hours. At the end of that time you will repay The Cid in our presence or suffer banishment and confiscation of all your lands!"

When the court gathered again three hours later, a ripple of laughter spread through the assemblage to see the proud Counts of Carrión leading in a long train of heavily laden mules and donkeys. These beasts were loaded with rich furs, weapons, jewels and goods of all kinds. The Counts had put their lands up as security to gather these riches from the merchants of Toledo.

"Do you, Rodrigo de Vivar, accept these chattels and goods in repayment of the treasure those of Carrión stole from you?" the oldest judge demanded.

"I do," Rodrigo replied. He signalled to some of his men who now came forward to lead the train of mules and donkeys from the field. Then The Cid turned once again to the court. He saw that although the Counts of Carrión were flushed with shame and anger, yet their faces showed also a certain sense of relief. They thought now that the worst was past. Rodrigo smiled grimly. "Sire," he declared, "my business at this court is not yet finished. I and mine have suffered deep personal injury and insult at the hands of these Counts of Carrión. You all know how they cruelly whipped and abandoned my daughters in the wild mountains of Corpes. I defame them here as cowards and traitors and ask judgment against their bodies."

Diego spoke. "Your Majesty, all the world knows that this betrothal to the daughters of a vulgar adventurer was an insult to our blood and lineage. We returned the insult and have gained more honor thereby, not less."

"Sire," The Cid said, "it was by your suggestion that this betrothal was made. You will know best how to avenge this insult."

King Alfonso nodded gravely. "Only a Court of Honor can settle this question," he announced.

The Cid frowned thoughtfully. A Court of Honor meant personal combat against the Counts of Carrión. But as the plaintiff in his own cause, Rodrigo would not be permitted to fight. He glanced toward his knights when he heard a commotion amongst them. Suddenly two of them broke away from the rest and hurried over to him. One was Pedro Bermudez and the other Martín Antolínez. They walked right past The Cid, grinning, and faced the Counts of Carrión.

"You, Fernando of Carrión," cried out Pedro Bermudez, "I call you a cowardly beast! Before the sun sets tonight I will cut off your beard and hang it on my belt as a trophy!"

"And you, Diego of Carrión," shouted Martín Antolínez, "son of a long and ignoble line of cowardly dogs, prepare your soul. For before the sun sets tonight you shall return it to the Devil!"

These words of Pedro and Martín were well calculated. The Counts of Carrión could have sent others to fight in their places. But in the face of such public insults their anger overcame their judgment. Diego spoke for both of them, his voice shaking with rage. "As we have already humiliated this person you call The Cid, so will we deal with you, base born knights. Be honored to receive death at the hands of nobles such as ourselves!"

"Let preparation then be made for the combat!" King Alfonso declared.

Immediately the field was cleared, combat judges were appointed and the knights retired to their tents to arm themselves. Rodrigo had every confidence in Pedro and Martín. "My gratitude will be eternal for what you do this day," he said to them as they strapped on their armor. "We are really very lucky, Cid," Pedro replied. "Every one of your hundred knights wanted to challenge these Counts of Carrión, but we picked the short straws."

"You have saved my life on more than one occasion, Cid," Martín Antolínez said as he balanced a lance in his hand. "This is but small repayment of what we all owe you."

The Counts of Carrión meanwhile hid their nervousness and prepared for battle. Much advice was poured into their ears by their few friends. But since they would not have to fight The Cid himself, their confidence increased as the moment neared.

At last the royal heralds sounded their trumpets and the combatants stepped out into the field. At another blast from the trumpets they mounted their horses. Pedro Bermudez and Martín Antolínez waited side by side at one end of the field. Facing them in the distance were the Counts of Carrión, armed, mounted and ready. The judges then proclaimed the rules of the combat. He who left the field or asked for mercy would be judged the loser.

At a signal from the heralds, the four horsemen, lances poised before them, rushed across the field at each other. The earth shook beneath the drumfire of their horses' hoofs and when they met the shock was terrible. Fernando's lance pierced Pedro Bermudez' shield but did not strike into flesh. Instead the lance splintered and broke. Pedro's lance bypassed Fernando's shield and buried itself in the chain armor above Fernando's heart. If Fernando had not been wearing three shirts of mail he would have been killed. As it was, he was badly wounded and thrown from his horse. Pedro immediately dismounted and drew his sword. Fernando of Carrión continued to lie upon the ground as if dead. But when Pedro bent over him to see if he still lived, the false Count lunged at him with a hidden dagger. Pedro felt the blade bite into his arm—but this did not prevent him from bringing his sword down full force across the throat of his traitorous enemy. Fernando of Carrión died thus in the very midst of his own treachery.

Meanwhile Martín Antolínez and Diego of Carrión had both broken their lances on their first charge. With drawn swords they wheeled their horses about, each trying to strike a mortal blow. Steel rang against steel, and their swords flashed like fire in the sunlight. But finally, Martín's sword bit deeply into Diego's shoulder. Seeing himself thus wounded, Diego of Carrión struck not at his opponent but at Martín's horse, crippling the poor animal with one stroke. Martín was thrown to the ground as his horse fell, and the sword flew from his hand. Then Diego, without dismounting to fight honorably on foot, charged down on his helpless adversary. But Martín Antolínez was a veteran of many a battle. When he saw the count charging down upon him with sword raised on high, he jumped to one side at the last moment and grabbed Diego's foot from its stirrup, pulling him to the ground in a tangle of armor. With one quick and practiced movement he wrenched Diego's sword from his hand and drove it home into his enemy's chest.

Thus the Counts of Carrión, who had lived in dishonor, died dishonorable deaths. A great cheer went up from the multitude of assembled knights and nobles who had witnessed the fight. King Alfonso rose. "The tournament is decided," he declared. "God's justice has fallen to The Cid. I command now that there shall be peace between the family Beni-Gomez and Rodrigo de Vivar. He who breaks this peace by word or deed shall be banished! May God have mercy upon all our souls and upon our lands and kingdoms."

Rodrigo heard these words with great pleasure. He hurried over to his tents and carefully supervised the bandaging of his two wounded knights, praising them for their courage and daring. Later he would reward them with lands and castles. But for the moment all his thoughts were about returning to Valencia where doña Jimena awaited him with their two daughters. In the name of his men and himself he made a gracious speech of thanks to the judges and took a friendly farewell of King Alfonso.

The journey back to Valencia was as gay as the trip to Toledo had been grim. The knights joked and sang upon the road and their joyful spirits reflected the contentment Rodrigo felt in his heart.

Their arrival in Valencia was more joyful still. The people cheered themselves hoarse and all the bells of the city were rung. Rodrigo went first to the cathedral where he gave up thanks for their victory. Then he hurried to the palace where he found doña Jimena awaiting him wreathed in smiles.

"You were right, Jimena," Rodrigo said when they were alone at last. "It was better to seek justice than revenge. But why are you laughing? Come, tell me what amuses you so."

Jimena smiled. "Those Counts of Carrión with their boasting of their high and mighty ancestors! Rodrigo, do you remember that I predicted we would yet find noble husbands for our daughters? Know then that Prince Henry of Aragon has asked for the hand of Maria, and Prince Ramón of Navarre wishes to wed Christina! Our daughters will be queens!"

Now The Cid's joy knew no bounds. He immediately dictated courteous letters to the Princes of Navarre and Aragon, arranging the weddings.

The following days were full of festivity for Rodrigo, his family, his knights and all the people of Valencia. But after the magnificent weddings had been concluded and The Cid's daughters had left Valencia with their royal husbands, doña Jimena found Rodrigo deep in thought one day, alone in his council chamber.

"What troubles you now, Rodrigo?" she asked.

"I was thinking of Diego," Rodrigo replied sadly. Then his face cleared and a look of determination came into his eyes. "I swore once that I would avenge his death."

"Rodrigo, haven't you learned that vengeance is useless?" Jimena asked. "You are not as young as you once were. You have your duties as King of Valencia to consider. We could be happy here, in peace."

Rodrigo shrugged. "What you say is true. If there were some way of exacting justice rather than vengeance—but who will judge an emperor? And there can be no lasting peace with Yusuf and the Almoravides. I tell you there can be no peace in my heart, either, until I have avenged my son's death."

Doña Jimena knew it would be useless to argue. But as she watched her husband's face she noted the lines of worry and care that had bitten deeply into it, and she saw the gray that was now creeping into his hair and beard. She felt a chill in her heart. But she showed nothing of all this and simply asked, "What will you do?"

The Cid rose. "The first thing I will do is call a council of state. And then, with God's help, I shall carry war and destruction home to the Almoravides in such a way that they will trouble our peace no longer!" His eyes glinted and his hand rested lightly on the jeweled hilt of *Tizone*.

How The Cid
Became a Legend

What The Cid wanted, more than anything else, was to provoke Emperor Yusuf into personally leading an army against him. In that way he would have a chance to strike at the chief of the Almoravides in person. But Yusuf was clever and would take the field himself only on the most important occasions, as he had at Sagrajas. Rodrigo discussed this problem at his council meeting.

"Why not take ship to Africa and attack this vile beast in his own lair?" Alvar Háñez suggested.

"Yes!" Gil Díaz's eyes sparkled at the thought. "There are ships a-plenty."

Rodrigo shook his head thoughtfully. "No. We are not yet strong enough to attack the Almoravides in Africa. If we were to destroy another of their armies, then they might be sufficiently weakened. And if we were to kill or capture Yusuf himself—then we could sail to Africa with good hope. A body does not live when its head has been cut off."

There was silence around the council table. Finally Martín

Antolínez spoke up. His arm was still in a sling from his fight with Diego of Carrión. "If I were trying to lure Yusuf into battle," he said thoughtfully, "I would attack that which he values most highly in all of Spain. He would be forced to come to protect it. If it were valuable enough he would come in person and not trust his armies to any other commander."

"Perhaps if we were to attack Granada?" Pedro Bermudez suggested.

"Or Badajoz," another knight added.

"Those are great and rich cities," The Cid admitted. "But we have seen how Yusuf entrusted an army to his nephew, Mohammed, for the protection of Valencia. And Valencia is as rich a prize as either of those."

Now Alvar Háñez spoke again. "It seems to me," he said slowly, "that we forget something. Yusuf is no lover of rich cities. He is no protector of the Moors of Spain. He has crushed them as if they were Christians. He has seized their cities too, but why? Not for the wealth they contain, but as bases for the conquest of all of Christian Spain. Yusuf is a fanatic. What is most important to him is his accursed Holy War. Endanger his military power in Spain and you strike at that which is closest to his heart."

The Cid suddenly arose, his eyes alight with inspiration. "Alvar Háñez speaks the truth!" he declared. "Murviedo! There is the place to strike! Murviedo is the strongest Almoravide castle in all of Spain. It is the very center and hub of all their operations. It commands the approaches to the Christian kingdoms of the North and to Valencia itself. Yusuf was willing to lose ten thousand men to capture it. It is his spearhead and stronghold in Spain. If we strike him there he will surely have to fight. If we captured Murviedo all his lands to the south would be in great danger. Murviedo is the bait that will lure him into battle!"

The council chamber was silent for a moment. Then Alvar

Háñez spoke again. "Murviedo is impregnable. It is defended by a huge garrison. Shall we lose ten thousand men ourselves to take it?" he asked quietly.

Rodrigo smiled. "Does the fisherman swallow his own bait?" He seated himself once again at the council table. "Let maps be brought!" he commanded. "Let us lay our plans carefully!"

Within two weeks The Cid had prepared a small army of five thousand men. He led them from Valencia at night and spread rumors that they were off on a raid into Granada. They followed the road to Granada that led past the great city-fortress of Murviedo, and early one morning not long after, its mighty walls and towers came into view. The Almoravides within the city, seeing that The Cid led such a small army, believed the rumors and assumed he would never dare to attack Murviedo. They simply closed their gates and waited for the Christians to pass by. But to their surprise they saw Rodrigo's men encircle the city and pitch their tents as if for a long siege. They were confident that The Cid could never storm the walls of Murviedo. But they had neglected to gather food and provisions for a siege. And they could not believe that The Cid did not have some huge army lurking nearby. In their confusion they sent off messengers to Yusuf seeking advice and aid. The Cid's men could easily have captured these messengers, but they had orders to let them get away.

Now the Cid sent for siege engines. There were giant catapults that could throw great boulders against the walls, towers on wheels in which soldiers could hide while they were rolled up against the battlements, huge battering rams and so forth. His small army presented every appearance of being determined to besiege Murviedo indefinitely.

When Emperor Yusuf in Africa received news of The Cid's intentions, he pondered the matter deeply. He could not afford to lose the fortress of Murviedo. But he could not believe that The Cid seriously thought of storming the place with a mere five thousand men. Then it must all be a trap! Perhaps King Alfonso of Castille was waiting with a huge army nearby. Perhaps the infidels expected Yusuf to rush to the defense of Murviedo and thus be caught between the jaws of two armies at once. Yusuf smiled. He was not so easily fooled. If the unbelievers had set a trap for him he would spring it on them! Calling his advisors to him, he ordered a huge army assembled. "The infidel dogs think to trap me before the walls of Murviedo," he announced. "But I will attack them where they least expect it. I will lead this army personally to seize Valencia itself. The Cid expects me to fight for Murviedo and so I shall— by seizing his own stronghold! Between Valencia and Murviedo I will crush this insolent Cid as one would crack a nut between two stones! We sail within a fortnight!"

Thus it was that the Emperor Yusuf led a mighty army—the flower of all his forces—in a sudden attack on Valencia itself. His fleet crossed the sparkling waters of the Mediterranean swiftly and landed his army on a sandy beach not ten miles from The Cid's capital. Then, to the sound of the dreaded Almoravide drums, this mighty host marched upon the city. Within a few days it was under siege. With The Cid gone, and his best knights with him, Yusuf expected Valencia to fall within a matter of days.

But Yusuf had walked right into the trap after all. For Rodrigo and his counselors had guessed exactly what the Almoravide emperor would do. They had known he would suspect the attack on Murviedo to be a trap and, putting themselves in Yusuf's place, had seen that an immediate attack on Valencia would be his best plan. They had prepared accordingly.

Inside this supposedly defenseless city, twenty thousand knights, heavily armed and under the expert leadership of Alvar Háñez, stood ready and waiting to receive the Almoravide blow. Meanwhile, The Cid, kept informed by spies of

Yusuf's every movement, waited until the Almoravides were firmly established before Valencia. Then, moving rapidly by night, he led his army from Murviedo and hurried back to the capital, bringing the siege engines with them.

Yusuf, unaware of The Cid's movements, ordered his army to attack at once. Wave after wave of screaming fanatics threw themselves against the mighty walls of Valencia. Alvar Háñez, within the city, had ordered his men to repel these attacks, but to pretend a certain weakness. By nightfall of the first day of the siege, Yusuf was confident that the city would be his within a week.

But that very night The Cid and his men secretly camped on the hills behind Yusuf's army. There Rodrigo ordered the catapults set up aiming directly down into Yusuf's sleeping camp. Then, when dawn came and the roaring Almoravide drums sent Yusuf's army once again to the attack against the city walls, The Cid ordered the catapults to open fire.

Never before had siege engines been used in warfare on the open field. It was the first use of a sort of artillery. When the great boulders crashed down among the tents and reserves of the Almoravide army, they thought the sky itself was raining destruction upon them. Their confusion and fear were increased by superstition. Yusuf now ordered back his advance divisions from the walls of Valencia to organize an attack upon The Cid's siege engines in his rear. But at that very moment, The Cid, leading his five thousand knights, charged down on the disorganized Moslems. And at this signal the great gates of Valencia swung wide to disgorge Alvar Háñez and his twenty thousand horsemen onto the plain.

Trapped between two powerful forces, their lines broken by the fury of the Christian charge, the Almoravide army began to disintegrate. When they heard the dread news that The Cid himself was upon them, their terror knew no bounds. This was

the terrible wizard who had drowned one of their armies. Now he caused boulders to rain on them from the sky! To fight against him was to fight against the Devil himself! Panic swept through Yusuf's army and it quickly fled desperately from the field, seeking cover from the terrible swords of the Christian knights and the even more terrible boulders from the heavens.

Rodrigo had spotted the personal banners of Yusuf flying beside a large and richly decorated tent. He rode for the spot, standing high in *Babieca's* stirrups, *Tizone* flashing in his hand, until he came upon Yusuf himself. The emperor wheeled his horse to defend himself. Their fight was short but furious. Yusuf was no match for The Cid and bent all his energies to warding off the terrible blows of *Tizone* and escaping from this terrifying enemy. But *Tizone* bit three times into Yusuf's flesh, badly wounding him. Rodrigo was about to deliver a death blow when suddenly *Babieca* stumbled over a tent rope and fell to the ground. Yusuf saw his chance. Without even attempting a blow at his fallen enemy, he simply spurred his horse to a gallop and fled from the field of battle. He was followed by a handful of his men. Riding as if they were pursued by the Devil himself, they fled to the beach where their ships waited. And it was not until he found himself a full league at sea that the Almoravide emperor drew a free breath.

The Cid's victory was tremendous. Of all that vast army of Moslems no more than a handful ever returned to Africa. All the rest were either killed or captured. The defeat at Sagrajas was avenged.

But although The Cid's army suffered few casualties, the cost was great to them. For The Cid, in falling from *Babieca*, had broken his shoulder. He was carried unconscious back to Valencia and put under doña Jimena's care.

When Rodrigo recovered consciousness he found his wife gently wiping his forehead with cool cloths. Her eyes were filled with tears and her face plainly showed the anxiety she could not hide.

"Why do you weep, Jimena?" Rodrigo asked gently. The pain in his shoulder made it difficult for him to move. "We have won a great victory. Sagrajas has been avenged. So Diego will be avenged, too."

"Rodrigo, you are very badly hurt. You must not think now of battles and vengeance. We have sent for doctors."

"No!" Rodrigo declared. "Send for Alvar Háñez. Call Pedro Bermudez, Martín Antolínez, Gil Díaz. Call all of my counselors. Now is the time to strike! Now we shall sail to Africa and finish these Almoravides forever! And Yusuf—he escaped me today, but one day he will pay for Diego's death!" Rodrigo closed his eyes as pain and weariness overcame him.

The Cid had been wounded often enough before. But his great health and strong body had always thrown off disease and weakness. Now he was over fifty years of age. The battles and campaigns he had fought had slowly but surely undermined his health. His broken shoulder became infected and within a few days he had fallen into a coma. The wisest doctors in all of Christendom were called to the champion's bedside, but to no avail.

From time to time Rodrigo would waken in a feverish delirium. Then he was heard to mutter such words as, "Diego, quick, there on the left flank!" as he imagined himself in battle with his beloved son by his side. Or he said, "Castille, never against Castille. . . ." showing that he still clung to his first loyalty. Once he raised his hands before his face and stared at them sadly and muttered, "Jimena will never forgive the death of her father." But Jimena embraced him and he turned to look at her. It seemed as if for that one moment he recognized her, for he smiled weakly and returned to his tortured sleep.

When it became apparent that The Cid could not recover,

Jimena called a priest to administer the last rites of the religion Rodrigo had defended so well. When the sacrament was concluded, Rodrigo spoke once again. "Spain," he muttered, "Spain united. . . ." They were the last words The Cid uttered. He fell back into his coma and the following morning, just as the cathedral bells were tolling the first mass, Rodrigo Diaz de Vivar returned his soul to God.

Great was the grief in Valencia. Knights and soldiers wept openly when they learned their great captain was dead. The entire city was plunged into the deepest mourning. And as the news spread from the city, sorrow and shock gripped every corner of Christendom. The mighty champion was dead! Who now would protect Spain against the hordes of Islam? Aragón, Navarre, Barcelona, Galicia, León and Castille felt the loss. They trembled before the storm which would now break over them, a tempest which The Cid had held back almost single-handedly. And beyond the borders of Spain—in France and England and Italy and the principalities of Germany—everywhere men felt as if they had lost their most powerful weapon in the desperate fight against Mohammedanism.

Doña Jimena's anguish was, of course, the greatest of all. But she showed her love and respect for her dead husband by overcoming it as quickly as possible. She knew that now the Almoravides would once again attack. And she knew that the greatest memorial anyone could raise to The Cid would be to hold Valencia for Christendom. She called together The Cid's knights and counselors.

"What shall we do now, Madam?" Alvar Háñez asked. "With The Cid gone the Almoravides will surely attack us. We are too few to defend this city against them."

"Yusuf will seek vengeance for his humiliation," Martín Antolínez added.

"If you would honor The Cid's memory," doña Jimena de-

149

clared, "you will defend his city to the last. I for one shall stay here, alone if need be."

"Doña Jimena, you are as brave as was your husband!" Alvar Háñez exclaimed. "Of course we will fight for Valencia! He who leaves now betrays The Cid!"

And so, with doña Jimena to lead and inspire them, The Cid's lieutenants planned for the defense of Valencia.

It was well that they did. For when the news of The Cid's death reached Emperor Yusuf in Africa, his joy knew no bounds. He had been desperately scraping together an army to repel the expected invasion. Now he saw that he would have time to recover from his defeat and time to raise another army to besiege Valencia. He felt like a man who has escaped sentence of death just before the axe was to fall. He threw all his energy now into organizing a new army to wreak vengeance on the insolent Christians of Valencia.

Within a few months the Almoravide storm once again broke over The Cid's city. Under Alvar Háñez's leadership, the defenders fought like lions, repelling every attack. Valencia had been well stocked with food during the previous weeks, so that when a great Almoravide fleet appeared doña Jimena and her advisors were not dismayed. They knew they had six months' supplies at hand.

But Yusuf, seeing that he could never carry the city by storm, decided to simply outwait them. If it was to be a month or six months or a year—all this was unimportant to Yusuf. He knew he had time to spare and the city's defenders did not. So he drew his siege lines as close to the walls as possible and then simply waited.

Now the Christians of Valencia had expected Yusuf to attack continuously and with great fury as in the past. Their only hope had been that he would then suffer such heavy losses that his army might be weakened enough so that they might have some chance of defeating it in open battle. But they could not outlast a long siege. Every day their supplies grew less and an hour would come when they must either surrender through starvation or be forced to offer battle to an army many times greater than theirs. In this extremity, doña Jimena sent messengers to King Alfonso of Castille. She wrote:

"If you bear any love for the memory of The Cid, and if you would best protect your own kingdoms, you will come to our aid in Valencia."

But the message was unnecessary. For Alfonso of Castille, as soon as he had heard of Yusuf's arrival before Valencia, had immediately started to gather a powerful army. Now that The Cid was dead, the Christian kings of Spain had finally learned the lesson of unity. In Alfonso's army were divisions from every kingdom, principality and city in Spain. It was a mighty host that he led to the relief of Valencia.

When Yusuf heard that Alfonso of Castille was about to descend upon him he was unafraid. In fact, he was secretly pleased. "We shall retreat from the troops of Alfonso as soon as they appear," he declared. "We shall retreat as if in flight. Then, when this insolent king and all his men are within the walls of Valencia, we shall suddenly return to the siege. We shall trap all the Christians in one place and utterly destroy them!" So saying, he sent messengers to Africa ordering forth reinforcements so that his army would greatly outnumber all the Christian forces combined.

It was on the hundredth day of the siege that a sentinel on the tallest tower of Valencia saw Alfonso's advance guard winding down through the mountain passes to the north. Immediately trumpets were sounded and the cathedral bells rung. From the walls, Alvar Háñez and his men saw Yusuf's besieging army strike their tents in great haste and retire in apparent fear from the field. The siege was broken!

When King Alfonso and his army entered Valencia the people went wild with delight and rejoicing. They had been snatched from the very jaws of death. They threw flowers down onto Alfonso's troops from the rooftops and celebrated a solemn mass of thanksgiving in the cathedral.

Doña Jimena and her advisors received Alfonso in the great council chamber of the palace. "Welcome, Sire," doña Jimena said. "You have saved this city and we are eternally grateful."

The king smiled and shook his head. "No, doña Jimena. It is you who by your great courage have saved Valencia. I promised this city to Rodrigo and to his heirs to hold forever. God grant that it may always be so."

But by the following morning Alfonso realized that he had walked into a trap. For Yusuf's men returned to the siege during the night. And where there had been forty thousand Moslem warriors there were now one hundred thousand. Valencia was encircled by the greatest army Yusuf had ever put into the field. Their ranks stretched for miles in all directions. And to make matters worse, the city, which contained little enough food, could never support Alfonso's army for more than a week. When the sentries reported the return of this huge horde of Almoravides, the rejoicing in the city was replaced by dread. Now it was apparent to everyone how Yusuf had outwitted them.

King Alfonso and doña Jimena at once called a general council. It was a gloomy meeting. To attack from the gates of Valencia in the face of Yusuf's huge army invited certain destruction. To stay within the walls meant death by starvation within two weeks. And with every day that passed new Almoravide divisions would certainly appear before the city.

"Are there any here who would defend Valencia?" King Alfonso demanded. He stared at the assembled knights who crowded the council chamber. There was no answer.

"None of you brave enough to defend The Cid's city?" doña Jimena asked.

"None of us, my lady, can perform miracles," Alvar Háñez replied gently.

"Once again I ask," Alfonso continued, "is there anyone present who would lead the defense of Valencia?"

But in truth the defense of Valencia was a hopeless task and none could be found who would undertake it.

"Then we must leave Valencia at once!" King Alfonso declared. "To stay here is simply to tighten the noose around our necks."

"It will not be easy to fight our way through the Almoravides," Pedro Bermudez observed quietly.

"It is our only chance," Alfonso replied.

"Will we leave the Christians here to their fate?" Martín Antolínez demanded.

"No," Alfonso said. "They will accompany us. No doubt many of them will perish. But they will all certainly die when Yusuf enters the city. This way they have at least a chance. And," King Alfonso turned to doña Jimena, "we will take The Cid's body with us. I shall never leave him here to be defiled by his enemies!"

Doña Jimena frowned. A thought had come to her with Alfonso's words. "Sire," she said, "I think perhaps I know a way to escape from Valencia without great loss."

Alfonso smiled skeptically. But as doña Jimena outlined her plan, the king's face became grave and intent. At last he slammed his fist down upon the council table. "You have spoken the truth, doña Jimena! Your plan is a good one. With the help of God and The Cid we shall yet escape from Yusuf!"

The following morning, at the first light of dawn, the Almoravide sentries saw the great gates of Valencia swing open. Instantly they sounded the alarm. Drums rolled throughout the huge Almoravide camp. Horses were mounted, weapons unsheathed. The enormous mass of Moslem warriors waited to throw themselves on the escaping Christians. Their spirits were high—this would be a massacre rather than a battle. Emperor Yusuf hastily mounted his horse. "Now," he muttered, "I shall slay them all. They will not pass beyond the first rank of my army. On this field Christian Spain will be destroyed beyond all hope of recovery!" He stared intently at the opened gates of the city, waiting to give the command that would hurl his army like a tidal wave upon the emerging Christians.

But suddenly a huge wail of terror went up from the advance ranks of the Almoravides. Mounted knights were emerging from the gates of the city. In their hands they bore the banners of The Cid. And at their head—no—it could not be! Yusuf cried out in surprise and dread. There was no doubt about it. It was The Cid himself who led the charge, mounted upon *Babieca*, his sword *Tizone* gleaming by his side! This was too much for Yusuf and too much for his army. The legends were all true! This Cid was really a demon from hell! Here he was, raised from the dead, charging relentlessly down upon them!

With wails of fear and screams of terror that rent the air for miles around, Yusuf's army fled. They did not even attempt to fight and neither did their emperor. Each of them thought only of escaping from the terrible apparition that thundered down upon them. They were certain now that the entire field was cursed and enchanted. A mighty wave of superstitious dread broke their ranks and sent them scurrying in their thousands in every direction so long as it led away from Valencia.

King Alfonso did not pursue the Almoravides. He recalled his knights who led back *Babieca* and the embalmed body of The Cid, which had been strapped into the saddle of his faithful horse. And it was thus, under the convoy of King Alfonso's army, that all the Christians of Valencia escaped from the city.

They made their way, protected only by the name of The Cid, to the safety of Castille. Doña Jimena's plan had worked beyond their greatest hopes. And although none of them knew of it, this final great victory of The Cid's, won after his death, fulfilled a prophecy made long ago by a certain grateful leper to a young boy on the road to Burgos.

So ends the chronicle of The Cid. What more is there to tell? When the Christians arrived safely in Castille, doña Jimena caused her husband's body to be buried in the monastery of San Pedro de Cardeña. When Jimena herself died, many years later, The Cid's body was moved to rest beside hers in the great cathedral at Burgos. There both tombs may be seen to this day. As for *Babieca*, The Cid's faithful horse, when he died Gil Díaz had him buried near the walls of Burgos. Two Alamo trees were planted on the spot and in after years they grew to a great height.

With the death of The Cid, the defenses of Christian Spain crumbled. The Almoravide armies regained the city of Valencia and pressed the Christian kings back into the northern deserts and mountains. It seemed that all of the labors of The Cid had been useless. Four hundred years were to pass before King Ferdinand and Queen Isabella finally drove the last of the Moors back forever into Africa.

But neither Rodrigo's life nor his works had been in vain. For with the death of the mighty *Campeador*, an imperishable legend was born. In the written chronicles of Christians and Moslems, in the songs of troubadours, in the tales told by gnarled peasants to their children and grandchildren it was told: How there had once been a knight of such generosity that even his enemies grieved at his death; of such loyalty that he bore undeserved punishments from his king without complaint; of such strength and valor that his very appearance put entire armies to flight; of such devotion and purity that God granted him a victory even after his death.

Through the years and the centuries The Cid came to be an example for each generation of Spanish youth. His spirit accompanied Cortes in the jungles of Mexico, Pizarro in the mountains of Peru, Don Juan of Austria at the great victory of Lepanto. Courage, loyalty, pride, and devotion—these have come to be the mark of the Spanish *hidalgo*. And this is the heritage left to his country by Rodrigo Diaz de Vivar, *El Mio Cid Campeador*.

A NOTE ON SOURCES

The legends and chronicles of The Cid have
been compiled from several medieval sources.
These include the *Carmen Campidoctoris* (Latin,
12th Century); the *Cronica Hebrea de Arevalo*
(Hebrew, 12th Century); the *Cronica del Cid*
(Arabic, 12th Century); the *Historia Roderici*
(Latin, 13th Century); the *Poema del Mio Cid*
(Spanish, 13th Century). While the authors of
some of these manuscripts are unknown, the au-
thenticity of the principal facts of the life of
Rodrigo de Vivar is beyond question. Whoever
has written on the subject of *El Mio Cid Campeador* must very gratefully acknowledge the
labors of the great Spanish scholar, Ramón Men-
éndez Pidal, who has done so much to establish
the veracity of his country's greatest legend.

159